£3.95

CONTENTS

PICTURE STORIES

STORIES TO READ

FEATURES ETC.

Printed and Published by D. C. THOMSON & CO., LTD.,
185 Fleet Street, London EC4A 2HS. © D. C. THOMSON & CO., LTD., 1992.
ISBN 0-85116-533-8

THE FOUR MARYS

THE Four Marys were good friends in the Third Form at St Elmo's. One Saturday afternoon in Elmbury they came across their old enemies, Mabel Lentham and Veronica Laverly.

BLOW! THOSE TWO ARE THE LAST PEOPLE I WANTED TO MEET.

YEAH. LET'S SNEAK PAST QUICKLY — THEY MIGHT NOT SEE US.

GOOD. THEY HAVEN'T EVEN LOOKED ROUND. THEY'RE STARING AT SOMETHING IN THAT SHOP WINDOW.

GREAT!

Next day —

BEFORE YOU ALL LEAVE THE SCHOOL CHAPEL, GIRLS, MISS CREEF WOULD LIKE TO MAKE AN ANNOUNCEMENT.

THE ANNUAL VISIT OF THE SCHOOL INSPECTOR IS TAKING PLACE AT THE END OF THIS WEEK. NATURALLY WE WANT ST ELMO'S TO LOOK ITS BEST.

A few days later —

HOW'S YOUR PAINTING GOING?

TERRIBLY! I'VE DRAWN THE CLOCK TOWER OUT OF PROPORTION TO THE REST OF THE SCHOOL.

MINE'S NOT MUCH GOOD EITHER. LET'S LOOK AT COTTY'S.

HEY — THAT'S BRILLIANT!

IT'S ACE! IT'S BOUND TO WIN.

HUH! I WOULDN'T BE TOO SURE OF THAT. MABEL'S ENTRY IS BRILLIANT TOO.

OH, DEAR! IT LOOKS LIKE I'VE A RIVAL.

MABEL'S NOT AS GOOD AS YOU AT ART.

But —

THE RUNNER-UP IS MARY COTTER, BUT THE WINNER IS MABEL LENTHAM, WHO PRODUCED THIS BEAUTIFUL PASTEL DRAWING OF THE SCHOOL.

WELL DONE, MABEL!

VERONICA WAS RIGHT. MABEL'S PICTURE *IS* BRILLIANT. NO WONDER IT BEAT COTTY'S.

MY PAINTING LOOKS QUITE AMATEURISH IN COMPARISON.

LOOK AT THE LIGHT AND SHADE ON MABEL'S WORK.

IT *IS* VERY GOOD.

ALL EXCEPT THIS CLUMP OF FLOWERS IN THE FOREGROUND.

WHEN THE ART COMPETITION WAS ANNOUNCED THEY CAME BACK AND BOUGHT THE PICTURE, SO THAT MABEL COULD PASS IT OFF AS HER OWN.

IT'S POSSIBLE, I SUPPOSE. IT WOULD CERTAINLY EXPLAIN WHY HER PICTURE LOOKED SO PROFESSIONAL.

ONE DRAWBACK. ALL THOSE PASTELS WERE SIGNED BY THE ARTIST — BRENDA BURNS. THE ONE MABEL PRODUCED WASN'T.

I'VE THOUGHT OF THAT, TOO. LET'S GO BACK TO SCHOOL.

THERE'S MABEL'S PAINTING — WAITING TO BE HUNG.

IF I JUST RUB THE FLOWERS WITH MY FINGER —

THE PASTEL'S RUBBING OFF — AND THERE'S A SIGNATURE UNDERNEATH!

MABEL DREW THE FLOWERS TO COVER IT!

THAT'S VERY INTERESTING.

MISS MITCHELL!

I ADMIRE YOUR DETECTIVE WORK. PERHAPS YOU WOULD SEND MABEL TO MY OFFICE IMMEDIATELY.

Later —

I'M BANNED FROM LEAVING THE SCHOOL GROUNDS FOR THREE WEEKS. IT'S NOT FAIR!

AND COTTER'S PICTURE HAS BEEN DECLARED THE NEW WINNER. IT'S BEING HUNG IN THE ENTRANCE HALL NOW.

AS A REWARD FOR HER DETECTIVE WORK, I WOULD LIKE SIMPSON TO HAVE THE HONOUR OF PRESENTING THE SCHOOL INSPECTOR WITH A BOUQUET ON HER ARRIVAL TOMORROW.

THANK YOU, MISS MITCHELL.

OOH! THOSE MARYS MAKE ME SICK! THEY LOOK SO SMUG. I'D HAVE BEEN THE ONE GETTING ALL THE GLORY TOMORROW IF IT HADN'T BEEN FOR THEM.

I'LL HAVE TO WEAR MY BEST UNIFORM.

WHAT A CARRY ON! BEST UNIFORM, BOUQUETS! YOU'D THINK IT WAS ROYALTY COMING, NOT A STUPID SCHOOL INSPECTOR!

IT WOULD SERVE THE MARYS RIGHT IF THINGS WENT WRONG FOR THEM.

THAT'S AN IDEA! COME ON, VERONICA! I'VE A PLAN!

LET'S LOOK AT THE CARETAKER'S OLD SHED. THEN I WANT TO GO TO THE FAR END OF THE GROUNDS — THAT PLACE CALLED HUNTER'S MEADOW.

Next day —

HOW DO WE LOOK?

FINE.

MY SHOES NEED A CLEAN. I'LL POP DOWN TO THE BOOT ROOM.

11

WAIT A MINUTE! A LOOSE PLANK! I'M SURE I COULD WIDEN THAT GAP AND SQUEEZE THROUGH IT.

As Cotty ran to the main entrance —

SOB! SOB!

THAT SOUNDS LIKE SOMEONE CRYING. I'LL GO AND SEE.

Meanwhile —

HA! HA! JUST WAIT TILL THE INSPECTOR TAKES A CLOSE LOOK AT THAT BOUQUET. SHE'LL JUMP OUT OF HER SKIN!

WHERE'S COTTY? SHE SHOULD BE HERE BY NOW.

HERE COMES THE INSPECTOR. OH! I DON'T BELIEVE IT!

WHAT?

IT'S DOCTOR GULL — OUR OLD HEADMISTRESS! SHE BECAME A SCHOOL INSPECTOR WHEN SHE LEFT ST ELMO'S. IT'S GREAT TO SEE HER AGAIN!

STEP FORWARD, SIMPSON.

WELCOME, DOCTOR GULL. I AM PLEASED TO PRESENT YOU WITH THIS BOUQUET OF FLOWERS.

THANK YOU!

OH!

IT'S CRAWLING WITH GREAT HAIRY CATERPILLARS! BUT I CHECKED THE BOUQUET HALF AN HOUR AGO. SOMEONE MUST HAVE TAMPERED WITH IT!

AH! I RECOGNISE THESE CATERPILLARS. THEY BELONG TO A RARE BUTTERFLY, ONE OF WHOSE FEW REMAINING NATURAL HABITATS IS HUNTER'S MEADOW AT THE FAR END OF THE SCHOOL GROUNDS.

RADLEIGH, WOULD YOU RETURN THEM THERE IMMEDIATELY, THEN NO HARM WILL HAVE BEEN DONE.

YES, DOCTOR GULL.

HOW PLEASED I AM, MISS MITCHELL, TO SEE THAT THE BUTTERFLIES ARE STILL THRIVING IN YOUR SCHOOL GROUNDS.

BAH!

BEFORE WE BEGIN OUR TOUR OF THE SCHOOL, I SHOULD LIKE TO DRAW YOUR ATTENTION TO THIS PAINTING. IT WAS DONE BY MARY COTTER, WHO SHOULD BE HERE TO TELL YOU ABOUT IT.

GOOD! CREEPY COTTER'S IN THE BAD BOOKS AT LAST!

HERE I AM!

COTTER! WHAT'S HAPPENED?

I FOUND THIS BOY LYING ON THE GRASS VERGE. HE'D FALLEN OFF HIS BIKE.

I'LL SEE TO HIM.

SO THAT'S THE REASON YOU WERE LATE, COTTER — BECAUSE YOU STOPPED TO HELP SOMEONE.

After the inspection —

ST ELMO'S PASSES WITH FLYING COLOURS! IT'S OBVIOUS TO ME THAT THE SCHOOL STILL MAINTAINS ITS TRADITION OF PROTECTING THE ENVIRONMENT AND HELPING OTHER PEOPLE. I'M DELIGHTED.

HUH! OUR PLANS WENT WRONG. DOCTOR GULL WAS ACTUALLY PLEASED TO SEE THOSE CREEPY CATERPILLARS, AND STUPID COTTER ESCAPED AND WORMED HER WAY BACK INTO THE GOOD BOOKS.

NEVER MIND. LET'S ENJOY THESE YUMMY CAKES.

OH, NO, YOU DON'T! THE CARETAKER TELLS ME HE SAW YOU DRAGGING COTTER OFF SOMEWHERE EARLIER. COME TO MY STUDY AND EXPLAIN YOURSELVES!

THE SNOBS ARE IN TROUBLE AND THEY DESERVE IT! THEY TRIED TO SPOIL THE DAY. I'M GLAD THEIR PLANS WENT WRONG.

FORGET ABOUT THEM. LET'S GO AND TALK TO DOCTOR GULL.

DO YOU REMEMBER WHEN SHE WAS HEADMISTRESS? WE HAD SOME GREAT TIMES AT ST ELMO'S THEN.

WE STILL DO!

THAT'S RIGHT. AND I'VE A FEELING THERE'LL BE A LOT MORE GREAT TIMES TO COME. HERE'S TO THE FUTURE — MAY IT BE AS GOOD AS THE PAST!

THE END

BUNTY—
A Girl Like You

A DREAM COME TRUE!

Most people only ever dream of visiting Florida's Walt Disney World. But sometimes dreams DO come true. Jenny Wilson, one of our Bunty Bug T-shirt models, tells us all about her trip of a lifetime!

"A trip down Main Street, where all the parades take place. You can buy and eat almost anything here."

"Here's the most famous duck in the world meeting the most famous bug! Donald Duck came rushing up to me when he saw my T-shirt! He really is quackers!"

"If you like shopping you've just got to head for the Disney Village Marketplace. There's so much to buy, it's impossible to make up your mind. I want to take ALL these characters home!"

"I loved Cinderella Castle! It's huge — 180 ft high — and there are massive mosaic panels inside showing scenes from the Cinderella fairytale. Cinderella Castle is supposed to be the most photographed building ever!"

"This is Starland — created for Mickey Mouse's 60th birthday. I wonder if he's home?"

"Well, that's about it. It would take up an entire Bunty Annual to show you all my photographs. It was a great experience and I've lots of brilliant memories to look back on."

16

18

THERE! NOW I'LL RING FOR THE SERVANT.

EMMA! THE FIRE HAS GONE OUT AGAIN. SEE TO IT IMMEDIATELY.

YES, LADY GWENDOLINE.

HOW CAN IT HAVE GONE OUT SO SOON? IT WAS FINE A FEW MINUTES AGO.

THESE COALS ARE DAMP, AND THE WATER JUG'S EMPTY. LADY GWENDOLINE MUST HAVE PUT IT OUT ON PURPOSE — WHAT A SPITEFUL THING TO DO.

NOW DRAW THE CURTAINS FOR ME. I'M GOING TO HAVE A LIE DOWN. IT'S VERY TIRING BEING A LADY.

NOT HALF AS TIRING AS BEING A MAID, I'M SURE!

Lady Gwendoline dozed off. A little later —

WHAT'S THAT NOISE? IT SOUNDS LIKE A CARRIAGE. OH, GOOD! WE'VE A VISITOR.

DOCTOR ROPER — THIS IS A PLEASANT SURPRISE! BUT WHAT BRINGS YOU HERE? WE ARE ALL QUITE WELL.

I'M PLEASED TO HEAR IT, LADY PARKER-RICE. BUT I WANTED TO HAVE A QUIET TALK WITH YOU — ABOUT LADY GWENDOLINE.

BOTHER! THEY'VE SHUT THE DOOR! STILL, I CAN HEAR PERFECTLY WELL WHAT THEY'RE SAYING ABOUT ME FROM OUT HERE.

DO YOU REMEMBER THE NURSE WHO ATTENDED YOU WHEN GWENDOLINE WAS BORN? A MRS WICKEN FROM THE VILLAGE.

YES, I REMEMBER HER, DOCTOR.

MRS WICKEN HAS RECENTLY DIED, AND ON HER DEATH-BED SHE MADE AN ASTONISHING CONFESSION TO ME. IT SEEMS THAT AT THE TIME YOU HAD GWENDOLINE, MRS WICKEN'S SISTER WAS ALSO DELIVERED OF A DAUGHTER, A GIRL CALLED EMMA.

THAT'S EMMA — OUR MAID.

"That is correct. She was a sickly babe."

POOR MITE! THIS ONE NEEDS EXTRA WARMTH AND NOURISHMENT OR SHE'LL SURELY DIE.

BUT WHERE WILL SHE GET THAT HERE? OUR COTTAGE IS COLD AND DAMP, AND THERE'S SCARCE ENOUGH FOOD FOR US ALL AS IT IS. MY BABY IS DOOMED!

MAYBE NOT. I'VE A PLAN. MY MISTRESS, LADY CAROLINE, HAS JUST HAD A STRONG HEALTHY DAUGHTER. I'LL SWOP THE BABIES OVER FOR A WHILE! LADY CAROLINE'S CHILD WILL NOT DIE HERE, AND YOUR POOR SICKLY BABE WILL BE WELL LOOKED AFTER AT THE BIG HOUSE.

MRS WICKEN TOLD ME THAT SHE DID SWOP THE BABIES. YOU WERE TOO ILL TO NOTICE. BUT THEN LATER, WHEN THE SICKLY CHILD HAD GROWN WELL AND STRONG, THERE WAS NO CHANCE TO SWOP THEM BACK.

YOU — YOU MEAN THE SERVING WENCH, EMMA, IS REALLY MY DAUGHTER, AND THE GIRL I'VE CHERISHED ALL THESE YEARS IS A PAUPER'S CHILD?

20

LOOK AT MY HAIR! IT'S COME LOOSE ALREADY! WHAT A CARELESS CREATURE YOU ARE. YOU'D BETTER START ALL OVER AGAIN!

SHE DID THAT ON PURPOSE! JUST LIKE I USED TO MAKE HER DO THINGS TWICE. SHE'S GETTING HER OWN BACK.

By tea-time —

I CAN'T GO ON. I'M EXHAUSTED. I MUST CLOSE MY EYES FOR A SECOND . . .

GWENNIE! WAKE UP . . .

. . . WAKE UP! WAKE UP!

I-I'M SORRY! I FELL ASLEEP. OH! WHERE AM I?

IN YOUR BEDROOM OF COURSE, MY DARLING. YOU'VE HAD A LITTLE NAP. TIME TO GET UP FOR TEA NOW.

IT-IT WAS ALL JUST A DREAM! OH, THANK GOODNESS! I AM STILL LADY GWENDOLINE, AND EMMA IS THE MAID.

YOU RANG, MY LADY?

YES. FETCH MY SHOES, EMMA. THEY'RE OVER THERE.

BUT WHERE WILL I FIND ANOTHER COACH?

OF COURSE NOT! BUT I'M LEAVING THE WAY CLEAR FOR SOMEONE ELSE TO TAKE OVER. YOU NEED A MORE HIGHLY QUALIFIED TEACHER NOW.

IT MAY BE EASIER THAN YOU THINK! HAVE YOU HEARD OF THE GREAT MADAME BERNSTEIN?

YES! SHE WAS A SKATER ONCE HERSELF. NOW SHE COACHES SOME OF THE TOP FOREIGN STARS.

AND SOON SHE MAY BE COACHING YOU! LOOK UP AT THE CAFE WINDOW.

OH! THAT'S HER. IT'S MADAME BERNSTEIN!

THAT'S RIGHT. SHE'S BEEN ON A TOUR OF BRITISH RINKS — LOOKING FOR YOUNG TALENT, AND SHE SPOTTED YOU.

SHE WOULD LIKE YOU TO DO A PROPER AUDITION FOR HER. AND I HAVE IT ON GOOD AUTHORITY THAT, IF YOU DO WELL, YOU HAVE A STRONG CHANCE OF BEING TAKEN ON BY HER.

I CAN'T BELIEVE IT! WHEN'S THE AUDITION TO BE?

NOT UNTIL NEXT WEEK. MADAME BERNSTEIN WISHES TO GIVE YOU TIME TO PREPARE.

THIS IS LIKE A DREAM COME TRUE! ME SKATING IN FRONT OF A TOP INTERNATIONAL COACH! I MUST MAKE A GOOD IMPRESSION.

I'LL PRACTISE A NEW BEGINNING TO MY ROUTINE. IT'S A BIT WEAK THERE. GOLLY, AND WHAT SHALL I WEAR?

HOLIDAY ON ICE

28

30

31

LUV, LISA

I LOVE CHRISTMAS AND ALL ITS TRADITIONS.

LOOK, JEFF. THIS IS A PICTURE OF YOUR FIRST CHRISTMAS WITH US. REMEMBER NEIL DID SOME MAGIC TRICKS TO ENTERTAIN GRAN?

AND DRESSING THE TREE WAS GOOD FUN TOO. I WONDER WHEN WE'RE GETTING OURS?

I asked Mum . . .

DAD'S BUYING AN ARTIFICIAL TREE TOMORROW.

ARTIFICIAL? BUT WE ALWAYS HAVE A REAL ONE! IT'S TRADITIONAL!

THEY SMELL AND SHED NEEDLES EVERYWHERE.

BUT THAT'S HALF THE FUN.

FOR YOU MAYBE! I HAVE TO CLEAR IT UP.

HUH! SO MUCH FOR TRADITION!

BUGSY

THE SALES START TOMORROW AND I WANT TO MAKE SURE I'M FIRST IN THE QUEUE. I WANT A PAIR OF THE TRENDIEST BASEBALL BOOTS AROUND — AND THERE'S ONLY ONE PAIR LEFT.

GREAT! NO-ONE ELSE IS HERE YET. I'M SURE TO GET THOSE BOOTS!

Next day—

IT'S ALL BEEN WORTH IT! I'M GOING TO GET THOSE BOOTS! NO-ONE CAN GET IN FRONT OF ME NOW.

Then—

HEY! WHERE DID THEY COME FROM?

I'LL HAVE THESE BOOTS, PLEASE!

"What's wrong, Bugsy? Didn't you get your boots?"

YES, I GOT THEM . . .

. . . UNFORTUNATELY, MY FEET ARE SO SWOLLEN WITH BEING STOOD ON, I CAN'T PUT THEM ON!

THE COMP

DO you have the sort of teachers who don't let you BREATHE out of turn? We do here at Redvale Comp. This is Becky, by the way — Becky Sinden. And our form tutor Grim Gertie — Miss Grimstyle actually, but Grim Gertie suits her better — is one of the worst. I mean, my best friend Laura Brady and I were only discussing a really important subject — my birthday — when Gertie came down on us like six tons of bricks.

"**I**F you two don't stop chattering you'll find yourselves writing out a hundred lines over half-term!" she snapped. Old misery!

Just then, the bell rang. Four o'clock! We were free of Redvale Comp for an entire week! We grabbed our books and bags and happily bounded along the corridors and into the school playground.

"So, have you thought what you want for your birthday yet?" Laura asked as we left the school gates with Roz and my twin sister, Hayley.

"Yes," I said. "Jason Donovan."

Mind you, when I got home I wished I'd stayed out a bit longer — because IT was there.

Jaws on Paws.

Now don't get me wrong. I like dogs, I really do. But THIS dog — a fat, yappy Pekinese — belongs to our Great Aunt Marjorie and it spends most of its life asleep and snoring. Mind you, when it's asleep, you're lucky, 'cos when it's awake, has it got a temper!

And it's called Snookie. SNOOKIE, would you believe!

"Glad you're back, girls," said Mum brightly. "Great Aunt Marjorie has to go away for a couple of days and she wants us to have Snookie. I told her you'd be delighted."

"Do we HAVE to?" I groaned.

"Now, Becky," said Mum, "Great Aunt Marjorie promised she'd be VERY pleased with you if Snookie is happy and well looked after when she comes back for him the day after tomorrow."

Now that's a different matter. Great Aunt Marjorie is . . . well, loaded, and what with our birthday coming up and our party in three days' time . . . I'd have patted Snookie, if he hadn't been growling.

Next day, we had to spend the morning taking Jaws out for a walk — or in his case, a drag. Snookie is none too keen on exercise.

After many false starts and sit-downs, we got him as far as the park. We were passing the playing field when there was a yell of laughter and several of the boys from our form descended on us, led by those wallies, Hodge and Freddy.

"Cor, look, it's the terrible twins and they're taking the loo brush for a walk!"

"Taking it for a scrape, more like. You sure that thing's GOT legs?"

"Come on, Snookie," said Hayley loudly. "Ignore those silly boys."

Now, that was a mistake. They fell about laughing.

"SNOOKIE!!"

"Ahh, little Snookie-wookums!"

WE had to get away from Hodge and Co., so I tried yanking on Snookie's lead, but he dug all four paws in. A passing woman gave us a frosty glare and made some comment about cruelty to sweet, little, dumb animals, which set the wallies off again.

But we weren't the only ones hard at work that day. When we went round to Roz's later, we found her and Laura washing a neighbour's car. They both went a bit red when they saw us.

A SPECIALLY WRITTEN STORY

"Hi," I joked. "Earning tons of money to buy us our pressies? Ha! Ha!"

"What makes you think you're getting any pressies?" said Laura. "We're just doing a good deed, aren't we, Roz?"

Then Roz's dad drove up. He climbed out, and took an enormous cardboard box out of the car boot.

"Got the box you wanted, girls," he called.

"SSSH!" hissed Roz, flapping her hands frantically.

"What's THAT?" asked Hayley.

"Nothing," said Laura. "It's empty. Look."

"I'm going to use it to store some things in the attic," explained Roz. "Well — bye, you guys!"

Talk about a HINT! Ever get the feeling you're not wanted?

But their funny, secretive behaviour didn't end that day — as we discovered the next day, when mega-disaster struck.

Snookie ran away.

Or waddled away. In any case, however he did it, he just vanished.

We searched the whole house and garden, checking anywhere he could be sleeping, but we just couldn't find him.

"Great Aunt Marjorie's coming to collect him at four!" wailed Hayley. "What do we DO?"

"Find him, what else? Come on, let's get Laura and Roz to help us look. We need everyone we can."

But would you believe it — those two WOULDN'T help!

"Sorry, we can't," said Laura. "We've er — got to do Grim Gertie's history project this morning, haven't we, Roz?"

"We sure do," agreed Roz, and they scurried off, looking guilty — as well they might.

"See you at our birthday party tomorrow," I called after them sarcastically.

"Some friends THEY are!" snorted Hayley.

We tried up and down all the streets, but nothing. Then we tried the park, and there we met Claire and Nikki, from our form, walking their dogs, Boots and George.

"We'll help," Claire offered readily. "Boots is part bloodhound, aren't you, boy?"

We trekked round and round the park. The part bloodhound found several ducks on the lake to chase and several flowers in the flower-beds to dig up, and George found a Jack Russell to fight and a kid's frisbee to pinch, but there was still no sign of Snookie.

Then we heard a piercing whistle, and Hodge and Freddy sauntered up.

"Here, lost your loo brush?"

"Get lost, Hodgson."

Hodge shrugged. "Okay, if you don't want us to tell you we've just

seen it tied to a lamp-post outside Tesco's . . ."

"Hodge, you're brilliant!" I yelled.

We hurried over there, with Claire and Nikki, too — but Hodge must've been blind. There was a Peke tied to a lamp-post, all right, but it wasn't Snookie. It wasn't HALF as fat. What's more, it wagged its tail when we went up, which is something Jaws only does if you approach him armed with chocolate cake.

"It's hopeless," Hayley wailed. "It's half past three, and Aunt Marjorie will be home at four . . . what are we going to do?"

THERE was only one thing left to do — go home, and face the music. We'd have to own up that we'd lost her precious Snookie.

But as we trudged home, we got the surprise of our lives. Laura and Roz suddenly rushed out of the garden of a house near ours carrying a small, hairy, fat growling object!

"Hey, look what we found in the compost heap!" Laura called. "He was fast asleep and snoring! Is he the one you lost?"

It was Snookie all right. But was he in a state! He was covered in grass cuttings and old leaves and muck, and did he PONG!

"We've got fifteen minutes to wash him before Aunt Marjorie gets here!" I yelled. "Come on!"

But Snookie liked the way he smelt, and he didn't take kindly to us trying to bathe him. In the end it was quickest just to turn the garden hose on him, and then have a go at drying him off with Mum's hairdryer.

We'd just got Snookie dry when Great Aunt Marjorie arrived, and swooped on him and gathered him up, cooing lovingly.

"How's Mummy's good boy den? Has oo been a good Snookie-wookums for the twinnies?"

Great Aunt Marjorie reckoned that Snookie-wookums looked so clean and well and happy that we deserved a generous reward each.

"And here you are," she cooed, dropping a pound coin into my hand. "That's fifty pence for each of you. Come on, precious Snookie, Mummy take you home!"

A QUID! We'd been killing ourselves over that mutt for FIFTY PENCE each!

Oh, well — the main thing was, Jaws had gone — and next day was our party.

I know we're daft, but we even rang Hodge and Freddy and invited them along. After all, they had TRIED to help.

And as soon as Laura and Roz arrived at the party, we instantly forgave them all their secrets and their mysterious behaviour. 'Cos, do you know who they brought with them . . ?

JASON DONOVAN!

Well, let's be honest — a life-size cardboard cut-out of him. But it was brilliant!

Turns out they'd been working hard, washing cars and weeding gardens to earn the dosh to buy the giant, large-as-life poster — and that was how they'd come to find Snookie — Laura had dumped a whole load of grass cuttings on top of him! Then they'd cut the poster out, and stuck it on to cardboard — hence the box.

"Well, you said you wanted him!" giggled Roz.

"He's the guest of honour," I announced. "Come on, you gorgeous hunk, give me a kiss!"

"Any time," smirked Hodge, materialising beside me and planting a great, wet smacker on my cheek. YEEE-UCK!! Even birthday parties have their down side.

I have to admit, Jason was the centre of attention. He posed nicely for pictures with us, even if he WAS a bit on the quiet side. He didn't eat too much either, and he WAS sort of a stiff dancer — but how many of YOU can say he's been to YOUR birthday parties, eh?

Mind you — how many of YOU have loony best friends like ours?

THE END

Marjy's Majorettes

MARJORY MILLER watched excitedly as a top American majorette team performed on TV. She had been waiting for over a year to join a group of majorettes, The Batoneers, from nearby Salcaster.

THOSE MAJORETTES ARE BRILL! I'D LOVE TO BE IN A TEAM LIKE THAT!

Marjy practised all the time. Later, her friend, Gillian appeared —

HI, MARJY. THAT LOOKS GOOD.

IT'S A LEG WHIP, GILLIAN. I'VE BEEN PRACTISING IT FOR AGES. ANYWAY, I FEEL LIKE A BREAK NOW. FANCY A GAME OF TENNIS?

And so —

NO WORD FROM THE BATONEERS YET?

NOTHING YET. I'VE HEARD THERE'S A BIG WAITING LIST.

On Monday morning —

LETTER, MARJY. SALCASTER POSTMARK.

OH, THANKS!

IT MUST BE FROM THE BATONEERS!

42

I HATE BERETS! I THOUGHT WE'D HAVE TRENDY UNIFORMS!

AND HOW COME YOU GET TO WEAR A FANCY CAP?

THE LEADER NEEDS SOMETHING DIFFERENT. COMPLAIN, COMPLAIN! THAT'S ALL YOU TWO EVER DO — AT LEAST WE HAVE BATONS!

RIGHT, WE'LL START WITH SOME BASIC TWIRLS. THE PINWHEEL THEN THE FIGURE EIGHT. COPY ME, EVERYBODY.

WAAH!

I'M EVER SO SORRY, MARJY.

HA! HA! THEY SHOULD CALL US THE BREAKERS!

I'LL NEVER GET THE HANG OF IT.

OH YES, YOU WILL, NORMA. IT JUST TAKES TIME.

THIS IS A JOKE! WE'LL NEVER GET ANYWHERE — ESPECIALLY WITH *HER* IN THE TEAM!

OH, DEAR! NORMA'S HOPELESS AT MARCHING TOO!

43

I'VE AN AMERICAN FRIEND AT THE AIR BASE. SHE WAS A MAJORETTE IN THE STATES. SHE COULD LEAD US.

OKAY, LET'S SEE WHAT SHE CAN DO AND HAVE A VOTE ON IT.

BUT THAT'S NOT FAIR ON MARJY!

When Gillian told Marjy —

SO THEY WANT A NEW LEADER, DO THEY? LOOK! SOMEBODY SQUEEZED GLUE INTO MY WHISTLE. NO WONDER IT DIDN'T WORK!

I BET IT WAS MILLY! WE'LL TELL THE OTHERS AT THE NEXT MEETING.

But, when Milly was accused —

IT'S A LIE! IT WASN'T ME!

YOU COULD'VE DONE IT YOURSELF TO COVER UP YOUR BAD LEADERSHIP.

I CERTAINLY DID NOT!

Just then —

HI, EVERYBODY, I'M PATTY STREEP, MILLY'S PAL. I HEAR YOU'RE LOOKING FOR A NEW LEADER. SHALL I SHOW YOU MY ROUTINE?

WOW! LOOK AT HER!

I CAN GET MY HANDS ON UNIFORMS LIKE THIS FROM THE BASE COMMANDER.

SHE'S BRILL! SHE GETS MY VOTE.

MINE TOO!

WHAT CHANCE HAVE I GOT AGAINST HER?

The vote was taken and Patty won easily.

WELL DONE, PATTY! YOU'LL BE A MUCH BETTER LEADER!

YOU CAN STAY AS SECOND IN COMMAND IF YOU LIKE, MARJY.

OKAY.

. . . BUT ONLY BECAUSE I WANT TO KEEP AN EYE ON THINGS. PATTY SEEMS TOO GOOD TO BE TRUE!

So Patty was forced to stand down —

I WANT MILLY AND LOUISE TO LEAVE TOO. I DON'T WANT ANY MORE "ACCIDENTS" HAPPENING!

ALL RIGHT, WHO CARES? YOU'RE ONLY GOING TO MAKE A MESS OF IT ANYWAY.

But the girls were much happier under Marjy's command —

BRAVO!

THIS IS A HUNDRED TIMES BETTER. NOW THE LEADER AND TEAM ARE WORKING TOGETHER!

Afterwards —

JUST ONE THING BEFORE I GO, MILLER — I WANT THOSE UNIFORMS BACK!

THE UNIFORMS WERE GIVEN TO THE PIVOTEERS, PATTY, AS A GOODWILL GESTURE BY THE BASE COMMANDER, NOT JUST TO YOU! NOW GET LOST, AND TAKE MILLY AND LOUISE WITH YOU!

YOU TELL 'EM, MARJY!

YOU WON'T WIN THE COMPETITION ANYWAY! SO WHO CARES!

YOU WILL WHEN WE GET ON THE TELLY! YOU'LL BE GREEN WITH ENVY.

One of the first things Marjy did was to bring back Norma.

WE'VE BEEN TRAINING EVERY SPARE MINUTE WE HAVE. NOW NORMA'S AS GOOD AS THE REST!

On the day of the competition —

SOME OF THESE TEAMS ARE TOP CLASS! WE'LL NEVER BEAT THEM!

OH, YES WE WILL, MARJY. AND IT WILL BE ALL THANKS TO YOU.

Then it was the Pivoteers' turn —

THE CROWD LIKE US. WE'RE GETTING GOOD APPLAUSE. OH, I HOPE NORMA'S RIGHT.

When the results were announced —

LADIES AND GENTLEMEN, THE WINNERS ARE . . . THE PIVOTEERS!

WE'VE DONE IT! WE'VE WON!

HURRAY!

I PROPOSE WE CHANGE OUR NAME TO MARJY'S MAJORETTES IN HONOUR OF OUR LEADER!

I AGREE, GILLIAN.

THANKS, GIRLS — YOU'VE MADE ME THE HAPPIEST MAJORETTE IN THE WORLD!

THE END

Pretty As A Princess

D

50

Later —

HELLO, PRINCESS! HAVE A NICE AFTERNOON?

YES. I WAS CHATTING TO BETH AND MARION. THEY WERE TELLING ME ALL ABOUT THEIR HOLIDAY.

WE'RE THINKING OF GOING ON A TRIP ABROAD TOO, THIS YEAR.

YES. TO AMERICA.

THE STATES? GREAT! THAT'D BE AN ACE PLACE FOR A HOLIDAY.

WE'RE NOT GOING ON HOLIDAY, FIONA.

SIT DOWN, PRINCESS. WE'VE SOMETHING TO TELL YOU. WE'VE HEARD ABOUT A DOCTOR — A FAMOUS EYE SURGEON. WE DON'T WANT TO GET YOUR HOPES UP, BUT THERE'S A CHANCE HE MIGHT BE ABLE TO MAKE YOU SEE AGAIN.

SEE? OH THAT WOULD BE WONDERFUL! IT'S WHAT I WANT MOST IN THE WHOLE WORLD!

BUT WON'T IT BE EXPENSIVE TO GO TO AMERICA? I KNOW WE'RE NOT RICH.

WE'VE SAVINGS PUT BY, AND WE'RE PREPARED TO USE THEM — EVERY PENNY — TO HELP OUR LITTLE PRINCESS SEE AGAIN!

And so, a few months later, Fiona and her parents flew to America, and the operation took place —

HOW ARE YOU FEELING NOW, FIONA?

A BIT GROGGY, BUT I'M ALL RIGHT. WHAT ABOUT MY EYES, DOCTOR VANDERBERG? WAS THE OPERATION A SUCCESS? WILL I BE ABLE TO SEE AGAIN?

THERE'S EVERY REASON TO BE HOPEFUL, BUT WE CAN'T BE SURE UNTIL THE BANDAGES ARE REMOVED. THAT WON'T BE FOR SEVERAL DAYS YET.

51

52

53

54

55

Jealous Janice

LIFE wasn't bad for Janice Barratt, but she had one fault — she couldn't bear to see anyone do better than her!

AND THE PERSON I'VE CHOSEN TO BE FORM REP IS — ALISON JACKSON! JANICE BARRATT IS DEPUTY.

CONGRATULATIONS, JANICE! YOU'VE DONE WELL.

MAYBE, BUT ALISON'S DONE BETTER. *I* WANTED TO BE FORM REP.

ONE OF YOUR DUTIES IS TO COLLECT THE REGISTER FROM THE TABLE OUTSIDE THE HEAD'S OFFICE EVERY DAY.

AH! MAYBE THIS COULD BE MY CHANCE . . .

Next day—

HERE'S OUR REGISTER. I'LL SNEAK OFF WITH IT FOR A FEW MINUTES.

ALISON COULDN'T FIND THE REGISTER SO SHE'S GOING BACK TO THE CLASSROOM. NOW TO PUT IT BACK.

I'M SORRY, BUT I COULDN'T FIND THE REGISTER, MISS PHELPS.

PERHAPS THE HEADMISTRESS HAS IT. I'D BETTER GO AND SEE.

But—

IT WAS ON THE TABLE ALL THE TIME! YOU COULDN'T HAVE LOOKED PROPERLY, ALISON. REALLY, HOW CARELESS OF YOU!

In various ways, Janice continued to cause trouble for Alison. By the end of the week—

YOU WERE SUPPOSED TO WATER MY FLOWERS, ALISON, BUT THEY'VE ALL DIED.

BUT, MISS, I DID WATER THEM.

AND THEN I EMPTIED THE WATER OUT AGAIN!

THEY'RE BONE DRY. YOU COULDN'T HAVE DONE IT. I'M TIRED OF YOUR LAX BEHAVIOUR, ALISON. YOU WILL NO LONGER BE FORM REP. JANICE CAN HAVE YOUR BADGE.

YIPPEE! I'VE DONE IT!

I'LL GO SHOPPING TONIGHT AND BUY MYSELF SOMETHING TO CELEBRATE BEING FORM REP.

57

THESE TOPS ARE NICE! OH, THERE'S JULIET FROM SCHOOL.

JUST IN

HI! WHAT ARE YOU DOING HERE?

I WANT A DRESS, AND THIS IS THE ONE I LIKE. I'VE BEEN SAVING UP FOR IT FOR AGES. WHAT DO YOU THINK?

IT'S ACE.

IT IS TOO. IT'S NOT FAIR. JULIET'S BUYING HERSELF AN EXPENSIVE DRESS AND ALL I CAN AFFORD IS A MEASLY TOP.

HOW IS IT?

A BIT TIGHT. I THINK I NEED A BIGGER SIZE.

THERE'S ONLY ONE OF THAT STYLE IN THE BIGGER SIZE. IF I HIDE IT DOWN THE BACK OF THE RAIL . . .

NEW STYLES

I'M SORRY. WE DON'T SEEM TO HAVE THAT ONE IN A BIGGER SIZE. WE DID HAVE. IT MUST HAVE SOLD.

HA! HA! JULIET MIGHT HAVE MORE MONEY THAN ME, BUT SHE COULDN'T BUY WHAT SHE WANTED SO IT WASN'T ANY USE!

That evening—

GUESS WHAT, JANICE? I'VE BOOKED US A WEEKEND IN PARIS AT YOUR HALF TERM!

PARIS? THAT'LL BE FABULOUS, DAD!

GUESS WHAT? I'M GOING TO PARIS AT HALF TERM!

THEY LOOK JEALOUS! GREAT!

HUH! MIGHT HAVE GUESSED, PAULA — THEY'RE ALL PONY MAGS!

HER BOOKS ARE THE SAME. ALL ABOUT HORSES AND PONIES!

HERE WE ARE! BY THE WAY, I BOUGHT SOME NEW JEANS LAST WEEK. I MUST SHOW YOU THEM.

So —

THERE! WOULDN'T THEY LOOK GREAT ON HORSEBACK?

BUT YOU NEVER GO ON HORSEBACK, BOBBIE. YOU'VE NEVER RIDDEN A PONY IN YOUR LIFE!

THAT'S NOT MY FAULT. THERE AREN'T ANY STABLES AROUND HERE. ANYWAY, I'M CONTENT JUST TO DREAM ABOUT PONIES, READ ABOUT THEM, TALK ABOUT THEM.

WELL I'M NOT! PONIES, PONIES, PONIES! THAT'S ALL WE HEAR! I WISH THERE WAS SOMETHING I COULD DO ABOUT IT.

A few days later —

I GOT A LETTER FROM AUNT MYRA TODAY. YOUR COUSIN DENISE HAS GOT HER OWN PONY.

A PONY! I WONDER . . .

I'LL RING DENISE AND ASK IF BOBBIE CAN RIDE HER PONY — SHE'S ONLY AN HOUR AWAY BY BUS. THAT MIGHT STOP BOBBIE GOING ON ABOUT PONIES QUITE SO MUCH.

So, the following weekend —

IT'S REALLY KIND OF YOUR COUSIN TO LET ME RIDE HER PONY. IS THIS OUR STOP?

YES, DENISE'S HOUSE IS OVER THERE.

The End

64

SISTERS OF SADNESS

EMILY and Olivia Harcourt went to India with their parents, where their father worked as a doctor amongst the poor. However, during a fever epidemic, both parents died and the girls were taken to a convent.

THE LITTLE SISTERS OF THE POOR ARE VERY KIND, OLIVIA — BUT I DO MISS MAMA AND PAPA.

NOW THEY'VE GONE, WE HAVE NOBODY IN THE WORLD EXCEPT EACH OTHER. WE MUST NEVER BE PARTED.

MY DEARS, WHAT WE HAVE PRAYED FOR EVER SINCE YOU ARRIVED HAS ACTUALLY HAPPENED.

SISTER BARNABUS, TELL US, PLEASE!

AN ENGLISH GENTLEMAN AND HIS WIFE, MR AND MRS REVERE, WISH TO MEET YOU. THEY HAVE NO CHILDREN OF THEIR OWN, AND IF ALL GOES WELL, THEY MAY ADOPT YOU!

THE LITTLE ONE'S JUST PERFECT, REGINALD. SHE EVEN HAS A LOOK OF YOUR GRANDMOTHER ABOUT HER. WE'VE FOUND OUR DAUGHTER!

MRS REVERE, I DID SAY THE GIRLS WOULD NOT WISH TO BE PARTED.

JUST A SLIP OF THE TONGUE, SISTER BARNABUS. NOW WE'VE MET THE GIRLS, WE WOULD LIKE TO OFFER THEM BOTH A HOME.

THANK GOODNESS. I WOULDN'T HAVE GONE WITHOUT YOU, OLIVIA.

I SUGGEST THE GIRLS STAY WITH YOU BEFORE THE ADOPTION IS FINALISED, TO MAKE SURE YOU ARE ALL SUITED.

OF COURSE! BUT I JUST KNOW WE'LL BE ONE HAPPY LITTLE FAMILY.

YOU MUST ASK FOR ANYTHING YOU WANT. WE WISH ONLY TO SEE HAPPINESS ON YOUR LITTLE FACES.

YOU'VE ALREADY BEEN TOO GOOD TO US, SIR. OUR ROOM IS WONDERFUL.

AND OUR NEW CLOTHES.

SIT HERE BY ME, DEAREST.

SOMEHOW I THINK MRS REVERE FAVOURS EMILY, BUT MAYBE IT'S BECAUSE SHE'S THE BABY. I MUST BE GLAD FOR HER, IF IT HELPS GET OVER THE LOSS OF MAMA.

Time slipped by, and the adoption papers were signed . . .

NOW YOU ARE OUR DAUGHTERS, SO YOU MUST TRY TO CALL US MAMA AND PAPA. IT WOULD MAKE US VERY HAPPY.

THE ONLY THING I AM SAD ABOUT IS THAT PROBABLY WE WILL NEVER SEE ENGLAND AGAIN.

But, a few days after adoption —

WE ARE RETURNING TO ENGLAND, TO OUR FAMILY HOME, REVERE HALL. I'VE HAD ENOUGH OF THIS CLIMATE.

MAMA, THAT'S WONDERFUL!

NOW I CAN BE TRULY HAPPY.

SISTER BARNABUS, YOU CAME TO SEE US OFF!

I, TOO, WILL BE RETURNING TO ENGLAND IN A FEW WEEKS. HERE IS THE ADDRESS WHERE YOU CAN FIND ME, SHOULD YOU NEED A FRIEND. BE HAPPY, CHILDREN.

After a long sea voyage, they eventually arrived at their new home . . .

REVERE HALL IS SO OLD, AND BITS OF IT ARE FALLING DOWN.

HUSH, EMILY, YOU MUST NOT SPEAK LIKE THAT ABOUT MR AND MRS REVERE'S FAMILY HOME. IT IS DISRESPECTFUL.

DON'T WORRY CHILD, I AGREE WITH YOUR SISTER. THE PLACE IS IN NEED OF REPAIR, BUT SOON WE WILL HAVE THE MONEY TO BEGIN THE WORK, THANKS TO A LITTLE IDEA OF MINE!

MY DEAR HUSBAND IS SO CLEVER!

THIS IS YOUR ROOM, EMILY. YOUR SISTER'S IS UP ON THE NEXT FLOOR.

BUT WE'VE NEVER BEEN PARTED. THERE'S PLENTY OF ROOM FOR TWO BEDS IN HERE.

IT'S TIME YOU GREW UP AND LEARNED TO MANAGE WITHOUT YOUR SISTER. YOUNG LADIES OF QUALITY ALWAYS HAVE THEIR OWN PRIVATE ROOMS. NOW WE ARE BACK IN ENGLAND, WE MUST KEEP UP APPEARANCES.

YOUR ROOM ISN'T AS NICE AS MINE. IT'S SHABBY.

I DARESAY THEY'LL SMARTEN THINGS UP FOR ME, WHEN THEY CAN AFFORD IT.

THIS IS YOUR GOVERNESS, MISS BEALE, EMILY. WHILE YOU ARE STUDYING, OLIVIA WILL LEARN SOME SIMPLER NEEDLECRAFT. SHE IS TOO OLD FOR LESSONS.

I DARE NOT COMPLAIN, BUT THIS IS VERY DULL. ALL I SEEM TO DO IS REPAIR BED-LINEN!

EMILY HAS A PLEASANT TIME WITH MISS BEALE THOUGH. TODAY THEY'RE HAVING A NATURE WALK. I ENVY MY LITTLE SISTER THAT LOVELY FRESH AIR.

TODAY WE GATHERED PLANTS, AND DREW PICTURES OF THEM.

THAT SOUNDS AMUSING.

UURGH...

CLUMSY CHILD! THOSE ARE NOT THE TABLE MANNERS WE EXPECT FROM OUR DAUGHTERS.

LEAVE THE TABLE AT ONCE. YOU CAN EAT IN THE SERVANTS QUARTERS, BELOW STAIRS.

SHE JOGGED MY ARM! SHE CAN'T HAVE REALISED WHAT HAPPENED.

Several days later—

COOK, I'VE HAD ALL MY MEALS DOWN HERE FOR A WEEK. WHEN MAY I RETURN TO THE DINING ROOM?

NEVER! THE MISTRESS DON'T WANT YOU TEACHING MISS EMILY ANY OF THEM BAD TABLE MANNERS.

I MUSTN'T GIVE THEM ANOTHER EXCUSE TO SEND ME AWAY. FROM NOW ON I'LL KEEP IN THE BACKGROUND AND SAY NOTHING TO OFFEND!

But—

YOUR ATTITUDE IS DOWNRIGHT SULLEN AND INSOLENT. I WILL NOT HAVE SUCH BEHAVIOUR IN MY SITTING ROOM. YOU WILL REMAIN BELOW-STAIRS WITH THE SERVANTS UNTIL I SEE A CHANGE IN YOU FOR THE BETTER.

B...BUT...

THE MASTER SAYS YOU'RE TO START EARNING YOUR KEEP, SO YOU CAN BEGIN BY MOPPING THAT FLOOR. THEN THERE'S THE PANTRY TO BE SCRUBBED OUT.

IT'S WEEKS SINCE I'VE BEEN OUT OF THIS KITCHEN! I'M DESPERATE TO SEE EMILY! I'LL SNEAK UPSTAIRS WHILE I HAVE THE CHANCE.

ALL GOES TO PLAN, BEATRICE. NOW IS THE TIME TO CONTACT THE FAMILY SOLICITOR AND INVITE HIM TO MEET OUR DAUGHTER.

ALL TRACES OF THE OTHER BRAT HAVE BEEN REMOVED. JUST KEEP LITTLE EMILY SAFE AND HAPPY UNTIL AFTER THE SOLICITOR'S VISIT — BUT THEN WHO KNOWS WHAT DREADFUL FATE MAY WELL AWAIT HER?

IT'S PLAIN THAT EMILY IS IN SOME SORT OF DANGER. BUT THE REVERES WATCH HER ALL THE TIME, SO WE COULD NEVER RUN AWAY.

That night, Olivia wrote the most important letter of her life —

WE HAVE ONLY ONE FRIEND IN THE WORLD. THANK GOODNESS I SAVED HER ADDRESS. I WILL ASK THE BUTCHER BOY TO DELIVER IT.

The following week—

OUR FAMILY SOLICITOR WISHES TO SEE YOU. THERE IS NO NEED TO SPEAK TO HIM. MERELY SMILE AND LOOK HAPPY. IN RETURN, I PROMISE TO FORGIVE YOUR SISTER AND PERMIT HER TO LIVE ABOVE STAIRS AGAIN.

OH, THANK YOU, DEAR PAPA.

NOW YOU HAVE MET OUR DEAR DAUGHTER, I HOPE THIS WILL SATISFY THE LEGAL ENQUIRIES YOU HAD TO MAKE.

INDEED IT DOES. I WILL SET THE WHEELS IN MOTION TO ALLOW THE INHERITANCE TO BE MADE OVER TO YOU, AS HER PARENTS.

I DID AS YOU ASKED, PAPA. WHEN MAY I SEE OLIVIA?

PATIENCE, CHILD. JUST A FEW DAYS LONGER AND THEN YOU WILL BE TOGETHER — FOREVER!

Sometime later —

AT LAST! THERE IS NOW ENOUGH MONEY DEPOSITED IN THE BANK, IN OUR NAME, TO BUY A MANSION ABROAD!

I'LL HAVE NEW JEWELLERY! I'VE WAITED LONG ENOUGH TO BE RICH, THANKS TO YOUR FOOL OF AN UNCLE!

NOW WHAT ABOUT THOSE BRATS? THEY'VE SERVED THEIR PURPOSE. THEY CAN BE GOT RID OF!

BUT THEIR DISAPPEARANCE MUST BE EXPLAINED. A NICE BOAT RIDE IS WHAT'S CALLED FOR. A DROWNING WILL SOLVE OUR FINAL PROBLEM!

Olivia wasted no time —

COME WITH ME, EMILY. DON'T EVEN STOP TO GET YOUR COAT. I'LL EXPLAIN LATER, BUT JUST RUN FOR YOUR LIFE!

WHAT'S GOING ON HERE? COME BACK!

But —

I HOPE YOU'RE NOT LEAVING US — NOT UNTIL I SAY SO!

At that moment —

DON'T LAY A HAND ON THOSE CHILDREN!

SISTER BARNABUS! THANK GOODNESS YOU GOT MY LETTER.

Later, in the safety of the convent —

MR REVERE'S UNCLE WAS RICH, BUT AS MR REVERE WAS A GAMBLER, HE LEFT EVERYTHING TO ANY CHILD THE REVERES MIGHT HAVE. THEY LIED TO THE SOLICITOR, CLAIMING THEY ALREADY HAD A DAUGHTER. BUT HE INSISTED ON SEEING HER FOR HIMSELF.

THIS MEANT FINDING A DAUGHTER OF THE RIGHT AGE IMMEDIATELY. EMILY FITTED THE BILL, BUT THEY HAD TO TAKE YOU TOO, OLIVIA — AND LUCKY FOR YOUR SISTER! FOR THEIR PLANS INCLUDED DOING AWAY WITH THEIR 'DAUGHTER' ONCE THEY HAD CONTROL OF THE MONEY.

WE — WE WEREN'T MEANT TO HAVE ANOTHER CHANCE OF HAPPINESS AFTER ALL.

HAVE FAITH, EMILY. SOMEWHERE OUT THERE IS A GOOD COUPLE WHO WILL BE MAMA AND PAPA TO US! BUT UNTIL THEN, WE STILL HAVE EACH OTHER AND THAT'S ALL THAT MATTERS!

The End

72

HAGGIS

A rabbit

 WOOF

You're supposed to run, rabbit, run!

HAGGIS HAGGIS HAGGIS

That's not the way to fetch Haggis...

RUSTLE

Santa's been

can't wait...

OH, NO! another "useful" gift!

FALSE FRIEND

WELL DONE, DELLA. TOP MARKS FOR YOUR MATHS HOMEWORK.

ALONG with the rest of her friends at Ellfield Comp, Jenny Parker found it impossible to like Della Pearson.

DOESN'T IT MAKE YOU SICK, JEN, THE WAY SHE PLAYS UP TO MR FRAYNE AND THE REST OF THE TEACHERS?

Even in Mrs Quick's class—

IT SEEMS THAT DELLA PEARSON IS THE ONLY ONE TO HAVE MADE A REASONABLE ATTEMPT AT THE HOMEWORK ESSAY ON THE TUDORS.

TEACHER'S PET!

IT'S A GOOD JOB THE TEACHERS DO LIKE THE LITTLE BRAIN-BOX, BECAUSE NOBODY ELSE DOES. I'M SICK OF HAVING HER HELD UP AS A SHINING EXAMPLE!

I KNOW WHAT YOU MEAN, KATH!

SEE YOU IN THE MORNING, JEN.

I WISH I DIDN'T LIVE AT THE OPPOSITE END OF TOWN FROM MY MATES. IT MEANS I DON'T GET MUCH CHANCE TO SEE THEM AFTER SCHOOL.

DELLA PEARSON'S THE ONLY GIRL WHO LIVES ANYWHERE NEAR ME — BUT THANK GOODNESS HER MUM PICKS HER UP. IT WOULDN'T BE MUCH FUN GETTING STUCK NEXT TO THAT SWOT ON THE BUS.

Then, a few days later—

WHAT AN IDIOT I AM! I'VE LEFT MY BAG SOMEWHERE AROUND THE SCHOOL WITH ALL MY BOOKS IN, BUT I CAN'T REMEMBER WHERE.

MAYBE SOMEBODY HANDED IT IN TO LOST PROPERTY.

Mrs Quick was in charge of Lost Property that week—

YOUR BAG IS NOT HERE. HOW VERY CARELESS OF YOU. I HOPE YOU REALISE THAT YOUR PARENTS ARE RESPONSIBLE FOR REPLACING LOST TEXTBOOKS.

OH — I — I'M SURE IT'LL TURN UP.

HOW ON EARTH WILL I DO THE GEOGRAPHY HOMEWORK WITHOUT A TEXTBOOK?

NO PROBLEM! GET YOUR DAD TO DRIVE YOU OVER TO MY PLACE TONIGHT, AND WE'LL SHARE MINE.

Dad agreed, but—

THIS IS A REAL NUISANCE, JENNY. YOU KNOW I'M BUSY IN THE EVENINGS.

I CAN'T TELL DAD MY BOOKS ARE LOST. HE'LL GO MAD IF HE THINKS HE'S GOT TO FORK OUT FOR NEW ONES. BUT WHAT WILL I DO IF THEY DON'T TURN UP TOMORROW?

75

OH, GREAT! SOME TERRIFIC PERSON'S FOUND MY BAG AND HUNG IT ON MY PEG.

OH, NO! EVERYTHING'S HERE EXCEPT THE TEXT BOOKS. SOME ROTTEN THIEF HAS NICKED THEM.

YOU'D BETTER REPORT THEM STOLEN TO MRS QUICK.

NO WAY! SHE'LL BE SENDING MY DAD THE BILL. OH CRIKEY — I CAN'T KEEP COMING OVER TO YOUR HOUSE. IT'S TOO FAR. WHAT'LL I DO?

YOU CAN ALWAYS COME TO MY HOUSE TO DO YOUR HOMEWORK. I LIVE QUITE NEAR.

OH — ER — THANKS, BUT I'M SURE I'LL MANAGE SOMEHOW. THERE ARE PROBABLY SPARE COPIES OF THE BOOKS I NEED IN THE SCHOOL LIBRARY.

IMAGINE — DELLA PEARSON INVITING YOU ROUND!

WHAT A MEGA-BORE *THAT* WOULD BE!

But later—

THERE'S NOT A SINGLE BOOK I NEED IN THE LIBRARY — THEY ALL SEEM TO BE OUT ON LOAN. THERE'S ONLY ONE THING I CAN DO!

ER — IS YOUR OFFER STILL OPEN, ABOUT COMING ROUND TO YOUR PLACE THIS EVENING, DELLA?

OF COURSE.

So, that evening, at Della's home—

YOU USE THE FRENCH BOOK WHILE I DO THE MATHS HOMEWORK, THEN WE'LL SWOP OVER.

And later—

IT WAS A NICE CHANGE, DOING HOMEWORK WITH SOMEONE ELSE.

BUT YOU ENJOY WORKING, DON'T YOU? YOU MUST SPEND HOURS EVERY EVENING, TO GET THE MARKS YOU DO!

THE ONLY REASON I WORK SO HARD IS THAT IT HELPS TO PASS THE EVENING. I DON'T REALLY KNOW MANY PEOPLE, SO I'VE NOTHING MUCH ELSE TO DO.

UNTIL YOUR OWN BOOKS TURN UP, YOU'RE VERY WELCOME TO WORK HERE EVERY EVENING.

94

I DAREN'T ASK DAD FOR NEW BOOKS SO DELLA'S OFFER IS THE ONLY ANSWER.

Then, one morning—

DELLA — WHAT ARE YOU DOING ON THE BUS? YOU ALWAYS GO BY CAR.

MUM'S NEVER FANCIED ME TRAVELLING ALONE, BUT WHEN I SAID I COULD MEET UP WITH YOU, SHE DIDN'T MIND.

PAY HERE

IT'S OKAY, ISN'T IT? YOU DON'T MIND?

ER — NO, OF COURSE NOT.

But, by the following week—

SEE YOU TONIGHT THEN, TO DO THAT HISTORY TOGETHER? WE CAN WATCH 'TOP OF THE POPS' AFTER, IF WE WORK QUICKLY.

SHE'S GETTING TO BE QUITE HUMAN NOW SHE'S COMING OUT OF HER SHELL. MAYBE SHE IS JUST VERY SHY.

But when her friends found out—

WATCH IT, JEN! GETTING FRIENDLY WITH SWOTTY DELLA PEARSON COULD DAMAGE YOUR IMAGE. YOU COULD END UP AS TEACHER'S PET!

OH, WE'RE NOT THAT FRIENDLY, HONESTLY.

DELLA'S SAVED ME A PLACE AT HER TABLE BUT I'LL PRETEND I'VE NOT NOTICED HER. I DON'T WANT TO RISK UPSETTING KATH AND SUE BY BEING TOO MATEY WITH DELLA.

That evening—

I WON TWO FREE TICKETS TO THE CINEMA, WOULD YOU COME ON SATURDAY?

I LIKE TO KEEP SATURDAY FREE IN CASE THERE'S A CHANCE OF SEEING KATH OR SUE. I'LL HAVE TO PUT HER OFF.

OH, WE'VE GOT RELATIVES COMING FOR THE WEEKEND. I'D BETTER STAY HOME.

OH, YOU DON'T HAVE TO MAKE EXCUSES JUST BECAUSE YOU DON'T WANT TO COME.

NOW I'VE UPSET HER. IF SHE DECIDES NOT TO INVITE ME ROUND TO WORK, I'LL HAVE TO ASK DAD FOR THOSE NEW BOOKS.

OH, ON SECOND THOUGHTS, THEY'LL ALL HAVE SO MUCH TO TALK ABOUT, THEY WON'T MISS ME. I'LL COME.

THAT'S GREAT. SATURDAY AFTERNOON, THEN?

But, just after lunch on Saturday—

DAD'S OFFERED TO TAKE US TO THE ICE RINK, SO WE CALLED TO COLLECT YOU.

OH, NO — I PROMISED MY MUM I'D STAY HOME AND TIDY MY ROOM. I — I DAREN'T BACK OUT.

I EVEN HAD TO LIE TO MY BEST FRIENDS. THEY WOULDN'T HAVE UNDERSTOOD WHY I HAD TO MEET DELLA. I'D MUCH RATHER BE SKATING THAN SEEING SOME BORING OLD FILM.

But surprisingly—

THIS IS A BRILL FILM. I DIDN'T REALISE YOU ENJOYED HORROR MOVIES.

I LOVE 'EM! WE'LL HAVE TO COME AGAIN.

COMING IN FOR COFFEE?

THANKS.

I'M ALMOST GLAD SOMEONE TOOK MY BOOKS. IF THEY HADN'T, I'D NEVER HAVE DISCOVERED THAT DELLA CAN BE REALLY GOOD COMPANY WHEN YOU GET TO KNOW HER.

OH, DELLA, WHEN I WAS CLEANING YOUR ROOM I FOUND SOME OF JENNY'S BOOKS HAD FALLEN DOWN BEHIND YOUR WARDROBE. THEY'VE GOT HER NAME IN.

OH, MUM!

MY BOOKS?

YOU WERE THE THIEF!

I DIDN'T SET OUT TO STEAL THEM. I FOUND YOUR BAG, BUT BEFORE I COULD GIVE IT BACK, I OVERHEARD YOU TELLING THE OTHERS THAT YOU'D NEED TO SHARE BOOKS IF YOUR OWN DIDN'T TURN UP.

I THOUGHT THAT IF YOU HAD TO SHARE MINE FOR A FEW WEEKS, YOU MIGHT GET TO KNOW ME A BIT AND WE COULD BE FRIENDS. SO I TOOK THE BOOKS OUT OF YOUR BAG — BUT I MEANT TO RETURN THEM EVENTUALLY.

YOU KNEW I WAS DREADING MY DAD GETTING A BILL FOR THOSE LOST BOOKS, BUT YOU LET ME GO ON WORRYING! A FUNNY KIND OF FRIEND YOU TURNED OUT TO BE!

But, on Monday—

CHEER UP, YOU'VE GOT YOUR BOOKS BACK AND YOU NEEDN'T BOTHER WITH GHASTLY DELLA PEARSON AGAIN.

BUT THAT'S THE TROUBLE. HONESTLY, SHE'S NOT THAT GHASTLY WHEN YOU GET TO KNOW HER.

IT MUST BE AWFUL TO BE SO LONELY THAT YOU'D PULL A TRICK LIKE THAT. MAYBE I WAS A BIT HARD ON HER. I'M GOING TO APOLOGISE.

YOU DON'T HAVE TO FEEL SORRY FOR ME. I THINK I REALLY KNEW ALL THE TIME THAT YOU WERE ONLY PUTTING ON AN ACT OF BEING FRIENDLY, JUST BECAUSE I WAS USEFUL TO YOU.

I'LL FIND A TRUE FRIEND ONE DAY, BUT IT'LL BE SOMEONE WHO REALLY WANTS TO BE MY FRIEND — NOT LIKE YOU, JENNY PARKER!

I ASKED FOR THAT. IT'S A PITY, BECAUSE I ENDED UP REALLY LIKING DELLA — BUT IT'S TOO LATE NOW.

THE END

Alpha Betty

HI, I'M BETTY. LIKE TO MAKE NEW FRIENDS? IT'S NOT QUITE AS EASY AS A, B, C, BUT I MANAGED IT!

A ALL ALONE ON AN APRIL AFTERNOON —

B BEST MATE BEV'S BEETLED OFF TO BIRMINGHAM. I NEED A BRAND NEW BUDDY.

C CATHY! COULD CHAT . . .

D DARLING!

DAVE!

DRAT!

81

E — EMMA?

F — FAY'S MY FAVOURITE FRIEND. FURTHER FAILURE.

G — GOT TO GET A GIRL TO GO GADDING WITH.

H — HER? HELLO!

I — I'M IVY.

J — JOIN ME! JUST JOGGING!

K — KEEN ON KEEP-FIT? KILLING!

L — LAGGING BEHIND. LOOKS LIKE SHE'S LEFT ME!

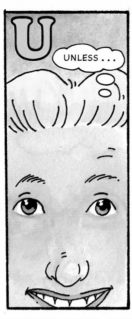

84

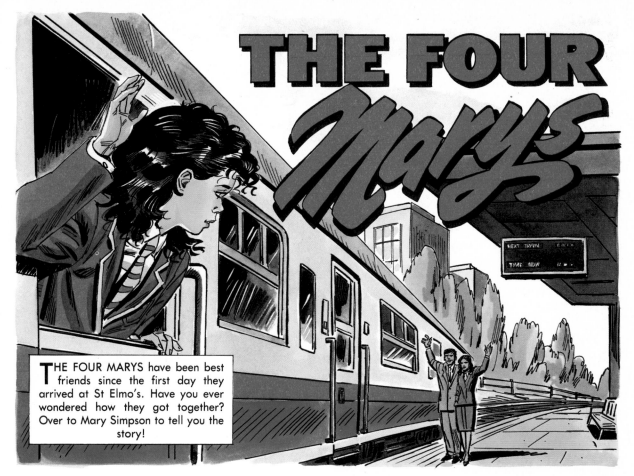

THE FOUR Marys

THE FOUR MARYS have been best friends since the first day they arrived at St Elmo's. Have you ever wondered how they got together? Over to Mary Simpson to tell you the story!

HI! Mary Simpson here — Simpy, to my mates. You might think my nickname's a bit daft but if you and your three best friends all shared the same first name, I bet you'd all have nicknames, too!

Anyway, Raddy, Cotty, Fieldy and I go to St Elmo's Boarding School for Girls. But we haven't always been pupils here — oh, no!

I come from a town called Ironboro' and I used to go to the local comp there — Grove Street. I guess my story really starts when, one term, to my delight (and utter amazement!) I came top in the school exams!

When I got home there was another surprise waiting.

"This is the prospectus for St Elmo's, dear. It's one of the top girls' boarding schools in the country," Mum told me, as she gave me a glossy brochure. "I wondered if you'd be interested in applying for a place."

I had a quick flick through the pages. St Elmo's certainly sounded great, but there was one big drawback.

"Mum, have you seen the fees for this place?" I asked.

I knew Dad could never afford to send me to a school like St Elmo's.

"It's okay, Mary," Mum replied. "Your headmistress explained it all to me. You'll get a scholarship grant if you pass the entrance exam."

Wow!

After that, things moved quickly. St Elmo's sent the exam papers to Grove Street and I did it there.

The papers were sent back to St Elmo's for marking. Days and weeks passed and I heard nothing. My friends and I had other things to think about, other topics to discuss — Grove Street's chances in the Ironboro' drama festival, the pop concert that was taking place in the Town Hall, who'd win a place in the school hockey team. I'd almost forgotten about St Elmo's and the exam.

Then, as I was setting off for school one morning, the postman stopped me and gave me a letter. My heart jumped when I saw the embossed badge of St Elmo's on the back of the envelope.

My hands trembled as I tore it open. Mum and Dad watched me anxiously. I read the words, then I let out a scream of delight and waved the letter in front of Mum. I'd done it! I'd won a scholarship to St Elmo's!

The teachers at school were really pleased for me. So were my mates. But I couldn't help feeling sad about leaving them.

"I'll really miss you," I said miserably on my last day at Grove Street. "I'm scared I won't make any friends at St Elmo's."

If only I'd known!

There was loads to do to get ready. Mum had been sent a uniform and kit list, and we went home from the shops laden! There were all my clothes, plus a new hockey stick, tennis racquet and swimming gear.

Mum and Dad came to the station to see me off. I'd been so excited the past few days with all the preparations, that I hadn't really thought what a wrench it would be leaving home. But seeing Mum and Dad standing waving me off on the station platform, getting smaller and smaller as my train pulled away from them, it suddenly hit me!

I was leaving home — my school, my parents, my friends, everything that was dear to me — for a whole new life. It was a terrifying thought. How would I cope?

★   ★   ★

When Mum and Dad were finally out of sight, I turned miserably away from the window. I think I might have started crying — but someone called out to me.

"Hi! Come and sit over here!"

I LOOKED round. At the end of the carriage was another girl in St Elmo's uniform, waving at me. She hadn't got on at Ironboro'. She'd obviously caught the train at an earlier stop, but — boy! — was I glad to see her!

"My name's Mary Cotter," she said as I joined her. "What's yours?"

I told her. Then she asked me about my previous school and my family, and she told me all about her background. Soon we were chatting away like old friends! The journey flashed past. I couldn't believe it when the train pulled into Elmbury station!

Mary Cotter and I picked up our bags and got off. But we'd only gone a few feet when Mary's suitcase fell open and all her belongings spilled out onto the platform!

Near us were two other girls in St Elmo's uniform. They both had short cropped hair — one dark and the other blonde. Seeing Mary's plight, I expected them to rush over and help. But they didn't!

"The shame of it, Mabel!" the blonde girl said haughtily. "That buffoon is actually coming to our school!"

The dark girl shook her head disapprovingly. "I don't know what St Elmo's is coming to, Veronica," she replied. "I really don't."

I didn't know it at the time, but we had just had our first encounter with the Third Form snobs — Mabel Lentham and Veronica Laverly.

Mary was scrabbling round desperately trying to push everything back into her case.

"I must have forgotten to lock it!" she wailed. "I'm such a fool! I'm *always* forgetting things or doing something daft."

By the time we got outside, there was quite a queue for taxis to the school. Ahead of us were a sporty looking girl with neat dark hair and a pretty, blonde girl. Judging by their uniforms, I guessed they were new pupils too. Then, in front of them, were the two I'd heard calling each other Mabel and Veronica.

At last the snobs reached the head of the queue. A taxi pulled up and they climbed in. The dark haired and blonde girl behind them moved forward to clamber in beside them, but Mabel put up her hand to stop them.

"Veronica and I prefer to travel on our own," she said snootily. "You lot can wait for your own taxi."

Then she signalled to the driver to pull away — leaving the four of us staring after it in disbelief!

"Of all the unfriendly things!" the blonde girl gasped.

Mary Cotter grinned at her.

"Never mind! We four can share the next cab," she smiled.

"Good idea! I'm Mary Field and this is Mary Radleigh," the dark sporty looking one replied.

"That's amazing!" I gasped. "We're both called Mary, too!"

"Four Marys! That's going to be a bit confusing," Mary Radleigh groaned.

We had ages to wait until another taxi came. But we didn't mind. The four of us were chatting away happily.

Mary Field told us she'd come from Webster's School for Girls — and I was right about her looking sporty. She was games mad! Mary Radleigh said her previous school was St Kilda's Preparatory. She told us the village where she came from too, but, typically modest, she didn't say that she actually lived in the local stately home there — Radleigh Hall, that her father was an Earl and that her correct title was really *Lady Mary*. I didn't find that out until the first parents' visiting day. Gosh! Was I surprised!

At last the taxi came and took us to school. It dropped us outside the gates. We walked up the drive together — Cotty and I in the lead, and Fieldy and Raddy behind.

I'll never forget my first ever look at St Elmo's. My heart skipped a beat! The building looked so huge — and grand!

Inside, the place was seething. Cotty and I soon found ourselves split up from Raddy and Fieldy. Someone told us where to put our luggage and we were able to have a wash and freshen up. We were just wondering what to do next when suddenly a bell rang and everyone dived for a door.

"Come on, let's follow them," I suggested. So we did, and found ourselves in the dining hall.

Everyone sat at long tables and, halfway through the meal, the Head Girl, Fairlie, stood up to make announcements. There was one about a drama group and another about hockey practice. Then she finished by saying that all Newts had to report to the Squawker! Cotty and I looked at each other in amazement. What on earth was she talking about?

I turned to the girl next to me. "What are newts and squawkers?"

"It's a St Elmo's tradition," she explained with a smile. "New girls like you are called Newts, and the headmistress is the Squawker!"

Cotty and I joined Raddy and Fieldy and the other new girls in the Head's study. When we first started at St Elmo's, the Head was Doctor Gull. She was older and much more traditional than Miss Mitchell, our present Head. As we got to know her, we grew to like her, but on that first day we were terrified!

We didn't need to be, really. Apart from going on a bit about not banging doors, she wasn't too bad.

We lined up to tell Doctor Gull our names and I remember Fieldy, Raddy, Cotty and I were in the front row. When we'd introduced ourselves, Doctor Gull told us that we were to be in the Lower Third, with Miss Creef as our form teacher.

Outside Doctor Gull's study,

Fairlie was waiting to show us round. First we went to the dorm, then the studies.

Fairlie explained that, at St Elmo's, it was four girls to a study, so she'd have to divide us up. She glanced at her list.

"I see there are four of you called Mary," she said. "You can be together — in here."

She pointed to a study. I peered in. It looked great! There was a fireplace, armchairs, bookcase, table and chairs, and a kettle and mugs.

After Fairlie had shown us round the rest of the school, we were left on our own to unpack. We soon had our study looking cosy and homely.

"I'll make some coffee," Raddy said, as we looked round, admiring it.

"Good idea! One sugar for me," I replied.

Raddy started rummaging — then she groaned. "Oh, no! I've forgotten the sugar," she said.

Cotter looked up eagerly. "I'm glad I'm not the only one who forgets things," she laughed. "Not to worry. I brought tea and coffee things too — just in case we could use them. The sugar's here."

She passed over a plastic container.

"Great!" Raddy grinned. "Kettle won't take long!"

Cotty picked up her empty suitcase. "I've just time to put it away in the dorm before we have coffee," she said. "Shan't be a minute!"

She hurried out of the door, but she'd only been gone a few seconds when there was a loud crash and scream. We ran out to the corridor to look.

Mabel Lentham was sitting in the middle of the floor, with a pile of sugar and fragments of a broken sugar bowl scattered all around. Cotty and her suitcase were in a heap beside her.

"You idiot!" Mabel screamed at her. "You ran straight into me! Why didn't you look where you were going?"

Fieldy pulled Mabel to her feet.

"Don't go on about it. There's no real harm done," she said.

"No harm done?" Mabel yelled. "She's broken my sugar bowl and spilled all the sugar. How are Veronica and I supposed to sweeten our tea now?"

"You can borrow some of our sugar, well — Cotter's actually," Raddy smiled. "I'm sure she won't mind. It's in the study over by the kettle. Pour some into a mug."

Mabel went over and busied herself at the table.

We nattered on for a bit, then Raddy said, "Oh, come on, this isn't getting the coffee made!"

But when we looked for Cotty's sugar, it was gone!

"Mabel took all the sugar!" gasped Raddy. "What a cheek!"

We dashed out of the study and along the corridor. As we got to Mabel and Veronica's, their door was open and they were chatting to a couple of cronies.

"That Mary Cotter is a fool!" Mabel snarled.

"And Simpson's so common!" Veronica replied.

"It's true," another girl agreed. "She's here on a scholarship, you know. She used to go to a comp, would you believe?"

"Definitely *not* St Elmo's material!" Mabel snorted.

I could feel tears welling up in my eyes. But Raddy put her arm round me.

"Don't take any notice," she whispered. "They're just stupid snobs. You're as good as any of us."

Then we listened as Mabel started to speak again.

"Let's drink a toast. To the new term!" she said.

"The new term!" the others echoed, and they put their mugs to their mouths to drink.

Immediately there was an awful coughing and spluttering.

It was Veronica who managed to speak first.

"What's in these drinks?" she asked, in a strangled voice.

"Only tea, milk and sugar," Mabel replied.

Then she grabbed Cotty's sugar container, dabbed her finger in it and put it to her mouth.

"It's salt!" she yelled. "We might have known! That stupid girl has brought salt instead of sugar!"

Outside in the corridor, Cotty gasped in horror at her mistake, but we all began to giggle. Stifling our laughter as best we could, we rushed back to our study.

Remembering the snobs' horrified expression when they'd tried their drinks, we all congratulated Cotty on her mistake and then burst out laughing again!

"Do you know something?" Raddy giggled at last. "I think we're going to have fun here at St Elmo's!"

And, as it turned out, she was quite right!

The End

BUGSY'S BUNCH

Penny's Problem Pony

PENNY SPENCER loved horses and ponies and spent all her spare time at the local riding stables.

THANKS FOR A GREAT RIDE, SUNBEAM!

YOU'RE GOOD WITH HORSES, PENNY. IT'S A PITY YOU DON'T HAVE A PONY OF YOUR OWN. HAVE YOU ASKED YOUR PARENTS?

HUNDREDS OF TIMES! BUT IT'S OUT OF THE QUESTION. THEY COULD AFFORD THE PONY, BUT NOT THE LIVERY STABLES.

However, a few weeks later —

WE'VE SOME IMPORTANT NEWS TO TELL YOU, PENNY. I'M BEING PROMOTED AT WORK. INSTEAD OF MANAGING JUST OUR WORKTON BRANCH, I SHALL BE IN CHARGE OF THE WHOLE NORTHERN AREA.

IT'LL MEAN MOVING, THOUGH.

OH! THAT MEANS I SHALL HAVE TO LEAVE MY SCHOOL AND FRIENDS — AND THE STABLES.

I KNOW. IT WILL BE A BIG WRENCH, BUT THERE *IS* ONE COMPENSATION, THOUGH.

WE THOUGHT WE'D LOOK FOR A COUNTRY COTTAGE. SOMEWHERE WITH A BIT OF LAND ATTACHED. THEN YOU CAN HAVE A PONY OF YOUR OWN.

OH, THAT'S GREAT! THANKS, MUM AND DAD! THIS IS MY DREAM COME TRUE!

A few days later —

MR BROWN! HOW NICE TO SEE YOU! WE WERE JUST HAVING COFFEE. DO COME IN AND JOIN US.

THIS ISN'T A SOCIAL CALL. I'VE COME TO COMPLAIN ABOUT THAT PONY.

OH, NO!

HE'S KICKED AGAINST THE FENCE THAT DIVIDES HIS PADDOCK AND MY GARDEN.

I'M VERY SORRY, MR BROWN. PENNY WILL MEND IT THIS AFTERNOON.

The next day —

WHAT A LOVELY RIDE WE'VE HAD! NEARLY HOME, KESTREL.

YOU CAN'T UNDERSTAND WHY I'M NOT RIDING YOU, CAN YOU, KESTREL? I'D RATHER BE, BELIEVE ME! JUST LEAVE THIS FENCE ALONE IN FUTURE AND HOPEFULLY THERE WON'T BE ANY MORE TROUBLE.

Then —

THIS LORRY'S GOING MUCH TOO FAST FOR THESE COUNTRY ROADS!

STEADY, KESTREL!

GET THAT ANIMAL OFF MY LAND!

I'M SORRY, MR BROWN! KESTREL'S FRIGHTENED.

94

So —

WE'RE GOING FOR A RIDE, KESTREL. NO, NOT THAT WAY.

I WON'T RISK PASSING THE BROWNS' HOUSE AND GETTING INTO TROUBLE AGAIN. WE'LL GO THE OTHER WAY.

And —

I'D RATHER BE GROOMING KESTREL OUTSIDE THE SHED BUT IT'S TOO CLOSE TO THE BROWNS' GARDEN. I'M AFRAID HE MIGHT START WHINNYING AND DISTURB THEM AGAIN.

Later —

GOODNIGHT, KESTREL.

A WHOLE WEEK'S GONE BY AND WE HAVEN'T HAD ANY MORE COMPLAINTS FROM THE BROWNS. KESTREL SEEMS TO HAVE SETTLED DOWN. GREAT!

But, later that evening —

WHAT'S ALL THAT NOISE?

IT'S COMING FROM THE PADDOCK. IT'S THAT PONY AGAIN!

OH, NO!

STOP IT, KESTREL! STOP IT!

HE'S CORNERED SOMEONE IN THE PADDOCK.

GET THAT MAD ANIMAL AWAY FROM ME!

WHAT A RACKET! WE EVEN HEARD IT ABOVE OUR TELEVISION.

AND DID YOU HEAR A BURGLAR RANSACKING THE UPSTAIRS OF YOUR COTTAGE, TOO?

WHAT ARE YOU TALKING ABOUT? WE HAVEN'T BEEN BURGLED!

WAIT A MINUTE! MY PEARLS! AND THAT'S THE BRACELET HARRY GAVE ME AT OUR GOLDEN WEDDING!

IT LOOKS LIKE THIS MAN STOLE YOUR VALUABLES FROM THE UPSTAIRS ROOMS OF YOUR COTTAGE WHILE YOU WERE WATCHING TV DOWNSTAIRS.

AND WE NEVER HEARD A THING!

HE'D HAVE GOT AWAY WITH IT IF KESTREL HADN'T CORNERED HIM AND KICKED UP A FUSS TO ALERT US.

I SUPPOSE YOU'RE RIGHT. IT LOOKS LIKE WE OWE THAT ANIMAL AN APOLOGY.

COME ON, YOU! I'M CALLING THE POLICE!

Next day —

ER . . . WE'VE BROUGHT KESTREL A PRESENT. HAVING HIM AT THE END OF THE GARDEN MAKES US FEEL MORE SECURE. HE'S BETTER THAN A GUARD DOG!

WE'RE ALL HAPPY NOW. THERE'LL BE NO MORE COMPLAINTS, AND I CAN CONCENTRATE ON WHAT I REALLY WANT TO DO — ENJOY BEING WITH MY OWN PONY!

THE END

96

SORRY! HUH! THEY'RE NOT HALF AS SORRY AS I AM. WE'LL NEVER BE A PROPER FAMILY AGAIN.

Mum tried her best to carry on as normal, but it wasn't the same—

WHERE SHALL WE GO ON HOLIDAY THIS YEAR? SOMEWHERE HERE, OR ABROAD?

I DON'T CARE.

I DON'T WANT TO GO ANYWHERE IF DAD ISN'T WITH US. HE USED TO MAKE HOLIDAYS SUCH FUN. OH, WHY DID THEY EVER HAVE TO SPLIT UP?

And the worst was yet to come—

MUM'S LATE HOME FROM WORK. OH! THERE'S A CAR PULLING UP OUTSIDE.

THANKS FOR THE LIFT, DAVE! I'LL SEE YOU TOMORROW.

SHE'S GOT A BOYFRIEND! HOW COULD SHE?

Mum denied it—

DAVE IS *NOT* MY BOYFRIEND. HE'S MY BOSS AND HE GAVE ME A LIFT HOME FROM WORK, THAT'S ALL.

HUH! I DON'T BELIEVE THAT FOR A MOMENT.

98

BUT EVEN IF HE *WAS* MY BOYFRIEND, IT WOULDN'T MATTER. YOUR DAD AND I ARE DIVORCED. I'M A FREE AGENT.

OH, WHY CAN'T MUM AND DAD GET BACK TOGETHER AGAIN?

But the months passed—

IT'S MUM'S BIRTHDAY TODAY, BUT DAD HASN'T EVEN SENT A CARD. I GUESS I'LL HAVE TO ACCEPT IT. IT *IS* OVER BETWEEN THEM.

Then, a few weeks later—

THE THEATRE? THANKS, DAVE! I'D LOVE TO GO.

MUM'S ARRANGING A DATE.

The theatre trip was a success—

AND AFTERWARDS HE TOOK ME FOR A MEAL — TO THE POSHEST RESTAURANT IN TOWN. WE HAD CANDLES AND FLOWERS ON THE TABLE!

THEY'RE GOING OUT AGAIN. THAT'S THREE TIMES THIS WEEK!

Then, at last—

SO WE'RE GETTING MARRIED, AND WE'D LIKE YOU TO BE BRIDESMAID! PLEASE SAY YOU WILL BE.

A BRIDESMAID? OH, YES! YES, I'D LOVE TO!

CHRISTMAS CRACKERS

That's what this page will drive you!

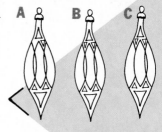

A B C

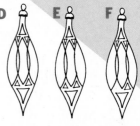

D E F

TREASURE TRAIL

Lead Bugsy through this maze to his presents, then unscramble what's inside them.

O R C
D R E S

K O B
S O B

L S E T
A C
C O O H

G S
A E M

C H E
V T S E

PARTNERS, PLEASE

Pair up these words on the left with their partners from the right. It's not as hard as it looks!

1. CHRISTMAS   A. LOG
2. SNOW   B. PIE
3. FAIRY   C. SACK
4. YULE   D. LIGHTS
5. MINCEMEAT   E. SPEECH
6. SANTA'S   F. TREE
7. GIFT   G. DAY
8. QUEEN'S   H. BALL
9. WRAPPING   I. TAG
10. BOXING   J. PAPER

MAGIC SQUARE

In this puzzle the last letter of each answer is the first letter of the next answer. Just work your way clockwise into the middle. S'easy!

1. This usually has a star or fairy on top (9, 4)
2. You always wake up at this time on Christmas Day (5)
3. A Christmas log (4)
4. It's tempting to do too much of this at Christmas (3)
5. You can decorate your tree with these coloured strands (6)
6. Candles give this to dark rooms (5)
7. You write these notes after Christmas (5, 3)
8. Presents are kept ----- the tree until it's time to open them (5)
9. The colour of Rudolph's nose (3)
10. You do this at parties and discos (5)

When they went back to the paddock —

HE'S GONE! I BET HE KNOWS HOW TO OPEN GATES. I SHOULD HAVE LOCKED IT, EVEN FOR THOSE FEW MINUTES. I HOPE HE'S GOT HOME SAFELY.

But when Sally reached Mrs Donald's house —

OH, FRAN, HE ISN'T HERE! AND MRS DONALD IS OUT. WHERE CAN HE HAVE GONE TO?

Fran seemed to know something!

FRAN'S GOING DOWN THE LANE THAT FRED WANTED TO GO DOWN EARLIER.

Then —

WELL! WELL! FRED HAS A FRIEND! BUT WHAT A POOR-LOOKING DONKEY. SHE DOESN'T LOOK AS IF ANYONE CARES ABOUT HER . . . AND HER POOR FEET — THEY NEED TRIMMING.

SO SOMEONE'S COME FOR JENNY AT LAST, HAVE THEY? I'VE BEEN WORRIED ABOUT HER SINCE HER OWNER, OLD JEM, WAS TAKEN TO HOSPITAL A FEW WEEKS BACK.

JENNY? IS THAT HER NAME? DO YOU MEAN NO-ONE IS LOOKING AFTER HER? I'LL TAKE HER HOME MYSELF, WITH FRED — IF SHE CAN WALK THAT FAR.

Jenny managed it —

WELL, YOU CERTAINLY DO COLLECT PETS, SALLY!

WELL, JENNY NEEDS SOME CARE, MUM, AND FRED'S FAR MORE SENSIBLE WITH HER NEAR HIM. I'VE AN IDEA FRED IS GOING TO BE EASIER TO HANDLE FROM NOW ON.

Sally was right!

DOWN NOW, FRED. GOOD BOY!

WITH JENNY CLOSE BY, HE REALLY PAYS ATTENTION TO WHAT I WANT HIM TO DO.

If you were to star in an episode of "The Four Marys" who would you play — a friend of Fieldy, Cotty, Simpy or Raddy? Or would you team up with Mabel and Veronica? Try our fun quiz and see!

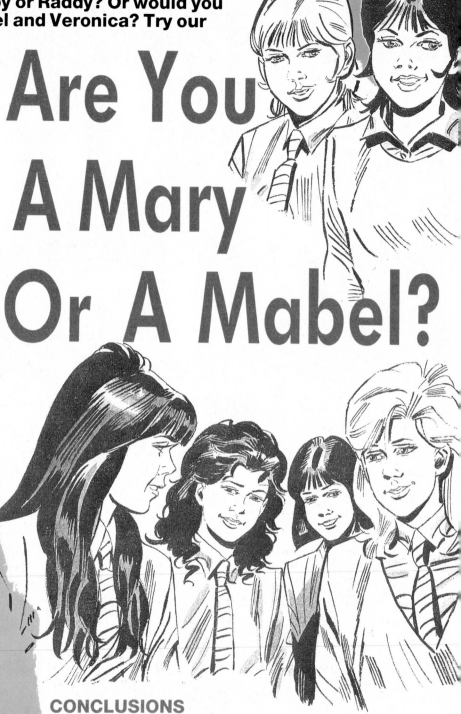

Are You A Mary Or A Mabel?

1. **A teacher asks for volunteers to clean out the book cupboard. What do you do?**
   A. Volunteer immediately.
   B. Wait to be forced into it.

2. **A big exam is coming up. What do you do?**
   A. Study harder.
   B. Hope you can find out the questions before the exam. You certainly can't be bothered studying!

3. **The school hockey team has been badly hit by a virus. They've used up all their reserves, but they still need one more player. Do you —**
   A. Offer to play, even though you're not much good.
   B. Do nothing — you don't much care about the hockey team.

4. **Some girls are misbehaving in class while the teacher is out of the room. Do you —**
   A. Try to get them to behave.
   B. Join in — it's only a bit of fun.

5. **The teacher has returned to the room and asks who started the trouble. If the culprit doesn't own up then EVERYONE will get detention. Do you —**
   A. Keep quiet and accept detention — after all, you would never sneak on classmates.
   B. Give threatening glances to the girls so that they have to own up.

6. **You are first in the queue for the tuck shop and there are only a few bags of crisps left until new stocks come in. Do you —**
   A. Buy one packet so that there's enough to go round everyone.
   B. Buy as many packets as you can afford, just in case new supplies don't come in.

CONCLUSIONS

Mostly A's
You'd be able to fit in perfectly with The Four Marys because you like to do your best to help people and to keep things running smoothly. Maybe you need to have a bit more fun though, 'cos some people might accuse you of being a goody-goody.

Mostly B's
Mabel and Veronica have found the perfect friend in you! You're just like them — rather selfish and capable of causing others a bit of trouble! Take a leaf out of the Four Marys' book and be a bit nicer and more thoughtful to others.

Miss Matchmaker

ONE evening, Cathy Taylor and her friends were visiting their mate Kim—

IT'S THIS SATURDAY YOUR SISTER GETS MARRIED, ISN'T IT, KIM?

YES, I'M HER BRIDESMAID — I'M SO EXCITED!

THIS IS MY BRIDESMAID'S DRESS.

IT'S BEAUTIFUL!

KIM WILL LOOK LIKE A PRINCESS IN THAT. I WISH I COULD WEAR SOMETHING SO PRETTY.

YOU'RE REALLY LUCKY, KIM. I HAVEN'T HAD ANY NEW CLOTHES FOR AGES. MUM'S ON AN ECONOMY DRIVE.

YOU SHOULD BUY YOUR OWN THINGS, CATHY. THAT'S WHAT I DO NOW.

REALLY? WHERE DO YOU GET THE MONEY?

BABYSITTING! I LOOK AFTER MY MARRIED SISTER'S LITTLE GIRL. SHE PAYS ME REALLY WELL.

ME TOO! I EARN A BOMB LOOKING AFTER MY TWIN NEPHEWS.

WHAT A BRILLIANT IDEA! THERE'S ONLY ONE THING WRONG — MY OLDER BROTHER AND SISTER AREN'T MARRIED!

STEVE DOESN'T EVEN LIVE AT HOME ANY MORE. HE'S GOT A JOB UP NORTH. BUT BEV DOES. IT'S A PITY SHE DOESN'T EVEN HAVE A BOYFRIEND!

I KNOW! I'LL GET HER ONE! IF THE BOY'S NICE ENOUGH SHE MIGHT EVEN GET MARRIED AND I COULD BE A BRIDESMAID! THEN LATER, I COULD BABYSIT FOR HER CHILDREN!

Next day —

HI, CATHY! WOULD YOU LIKE TWO TICKETS FOR THE ROCK CONCERT ON FRIDAY? MY GIRLFRIEND FINISHED WITH ME YESTERDAY, SO I'VE NO-ONE TO TAKE NOW.

YES, PLEASE. I'D LOVE TO GO, MIKE.

WAIT A MINUTE — THIS COULD BE MY CHANCE TO FIND BEV A BOYFRIEND! MIKE'S THE PERFECT BOY NEXT DOOR.

OH, I'VE JUST REMEMBERED I'M BUSY ON FRIDAY, BUT BEV ISN'T. WHY DON'T YOU TAKE HER?

OKAY. THAT'S A GOOD IDEA!

THIS COULD BE THE START OF SOMETHING GREAT!

On Friday —

HAVE A GOOD TIME AT THE CONCERT, BEV.

THANKS! I'M SURE I SHALL.

Late that night —

THE CONCERT WAS GREAT! AND MIKE'S GOING TO RING ME TOMORROW TO MAKE ANOTHER DATE.

BRILL! THEY'LL BE GOING STEADY SOON.

But, next day —

I'M SORRY, BEV, BUT AMY, MY EX-GIRLFRIEND, WANTS US TO GET TOGETHER AGAIN. I HOPE YOU UNDERSTAND.

YES. OF COURSE, MIKE. NO PROBLEM.

OOH! THE CREEP!

IT DOESN'T MATTER. I DON'T WANT TO GET SERIOUS ANYWAY. I'M MORE INTERESTED IN MY CAREER AT THE BANK RIGHT NOW.

I'LL JUST HAVE TO TRY AGAIN! I'M SURE BEV WOULD CHANGE HER MIND IF MR RIGHT CAME ALONG.

A few days later —

GRAN'S SENT ME SOME MONEY FOR MY BIRTHDAY. I'LL PUT IT INTO MY SAVINGS ACCOUNT.

NO SIGN OF BEV — SHE MUST BE ON HER TEA BREAK. H'MM. HE'S A BIT TASTY. I WONDER WHY BEV HAS NEVER MENTIONED HIM?

109

Cathy and Bev were both having birthdays the following week —

YOU CAN HAVE A JOINT PARTY — BUT JUST EIGHT GUESTS EACH. WE CAN'T FIT ANY MORE PEOPLE IN THE HOUSE.

THAT'S ACE, MUM!

ARE YOU GOING TO INVITE THAT DISHY BOY FROM YOUR BANK?

RICK MASON? NO, I DON'T THINK SO. I'VE ALREADY MADE UP MY LIST OF GUESTS.

THAT'S OKAY. I DON'T MIND GIVING UP ONE OF MY GUESTS SO YOU CAN INVITE HIM.

ALL RIGHT. BUT I CAN'T THINK WHY YOU FANCY HIM. HE'S FAR TOO OLD FOR YOU.

BEV'S GOT IT ALL WRONG! SHE'S THE ONE WHO'S GOING TO END UP WITH HIM! I'LL FIX IT UP AT THE PARTY.

But, on the night —

SO I CALCULATE THAT THE BASE INTEREST RATE ON A LOAN OF THAT SIZE . . .

WHAT A BORE! NO WONDER BEV'S NOT INTERESTED IN A GUY WHO CAN ONLY TALK ABOUT THE BANK.

GONE OFF RICK? I'M NOT SURPRISED! GOOD LOOKS AREN'T EVERYTHING!

SHE CAN SAY THAT AGAIN! I'LL HAVE TO FIND ANOTHER BOY FOR BEV.

WOW! ISN'T HE GORGEOUS?

GREAT! BEV FANCIES THAT BOY! I'LL MAKE HIM STOP AND THEY'LL GET CHATTING.

So —

HELP! I'M SLIPPING!

I'VE HURT MY ANKLE.

HE'S STOPPING! MY ANKLE'S FINE, BUT I CAN'T SAY THE SAME FOR MY LEGGINGS! STILL, IT'LL BE WORTH IT IF BEV AND THAT BOY FALL FOR EACH OTHER.

ARE YOU OKAY?

I — ER — THINK SO. I'LL JUST SIT ON THIS BENCH FOR A FEW MINUTES.

AND GIVE THEM A CHANCE TO CHAT.

WHAT'S YOUR HORSE'S NAME?

IT'S SILVER. I SEE YOU LIKE HORSES. WOULD YOU LIKE TO COME HORSE-RIDING WITH ME ONE WEEKEND?

HE'S ASKED BEV OUT AND I KNOW SHE FANCIES HIM TOO BECAUSE SHE SAID SO! I'VE SUCCEEDED AT LAST!

But —

ER . . . NO THANKS. MY SISTER SEEMS OKAY NOW. I THINK WE'D BETTER GO HOME.

WHAT?

WHY DIDN'T YOU WANT TO GO OUT WITH HIM?

BECAUSE I DON'T FANCY HIM.

BUT YOU SAID HE WAS GORGEOUS.

THAT WAS THE *HORSE* I WAS TALKING ABOUT, SILLY!

Back home —

YOU'D BETTER CHANGE YOUR CLOTHES, CATHY. WE'VE VISITORS.

WHO?

STEVE!

HI, SIS! MEET MY FIANCEE, LINDA. WE'RE GETTING MARRIED IN THE SPRING.

THEN WE'LL BE MOVING BACK HERE TO LIVE.

WE WANT A FAMILY AND IF WE'RE NEARBY, WE HOPE YOU'LL ALL HELP OUT WITH BABYSITTING WHEN THE TIME COMES.

I'D LOVE TO!

AND I'D LIKE YOU BOTH TO BE MY BRIDESMAIDS.

ALL MY DREAMS HAVE COME TRUE — EVEN THOUGH I NEVER DID FIND A BOY FOR BEV!

The End

The Comp

IT was end of term at Redvale Comp — but some of the Third Year pupils weren't going straight home for the holidays!

THIS IS GOING TO BE GREAT, BECKY. FOUR DAYS HILLWALKING AND HIKING — WHAT A RUN-UP TO CHRISTMAS!

THERE'LL BE WORK TO BE DONE AS WELL, LAURA. THIS IS A GEOGRAPHY FIELD TRIP, NOT A HOLIDAY!

TRUST MAD MAUREEN TO REMIND US OF THAT!

Hours later—

HERE WE ARE! EVERYBODY OUT!

WOW! IT'S MILES FROM ANYWHERE UP HERE!

Next day—

LOOK AT THAT FOR A VIEW!

YOU'RE NOT HERE JUST TO ENJOY THE VIEW. FOLLOW YOUR WORKSHEETS!

OLD GROUCH!

I THINK WE SHOULD FOLLOW THAT BRIDLE PATH.

NO, HAYLEY, WE'RE LOOKING FOR A CHURCH, AND THERE ISN'T ONE OFF IN THAT DIRECTION. WE SHOULD BACKTRACK AND TAKE THIS PATH HERE.

LUCKY ONE OF US CAN READ MAPS!

On the morning of the very last day—

OOH! WE'RE NOT GOING OUT IN THIS, ARE WE, MISS SMITH? IT'S RAINING!

SO PUT YOUR WATERPROOFS ON, AND STOP FUSSING, HAYLEY!

114

Y-YOU MEAN WE'RE STUCK HERE? HOW LONG FOR?

IT'S CHRISTMAS EVE TOMORROW! WE HAVE TO GET HOME!

DON'T WORRY. IF THE RAIN STOPS, THE ROAD MAY CLEAR . . .

WELL, THE RAIN'S STOPPED — IT'S TURNED TO SNOW!

STORMS GO ON FOR DAYS UP HERE!

W-WE COULD BE HERE — FOR CHRISTMAS DAY! NO FAMILIES — NO PRESENTS.

OH, NO . . .

Gloom descended on the party—

WELL, MISS SMITH HAS GOT THE CALOR GAS GOING, SO WHO'S FOR A MUG OF SOUP?

THIS COULD BE OUR CHRISTMAS DINNER — SOUP AND SANDWICHES!

OOOH, DON'T, CLAIRE!

HEY, DON'T WORRY. TWO CHRISTMASES AGO, I HAD BAKED BEANS FOR CHRISTMAS DINNER!

I REMEMBER. YOUR DAD WAS GOING TO COOK THE TURKEY, AND HE FORGOT TO SET THE OVEN-TIMER!

HA! HA! HA! SUPERCHEF!

RAW TURKEY, ANYONE?

QUIET, THE PAIR OF YOU!

"We had our dinner for supper that day!"

THAT WAS THE YEAR I REALLY THOUGHT MY MOM AND DAD WERE GETTING BACK TOGETHER . . . BUT MOM WENT BACK TO THE STATES.

BOTHER, I DIDN'T MEAN ROZ TO REMEMBER THAT . . .

HEY, REMEMBER LAST CHRISTMAS? NIKKI'S MUM'S BABY WASN'T DUE TILL WELL AFTER THE NEW YEAR, BUT —

On the last day of term—

SHE'S COME! SHE'S HERE FIVE WEEKS EARLY! I'VE GOT A LITTLE SISTER! HER NAME'S ELIZABETH!

NICE ONE, NIK! GRIM GERTIE WAS ABOUT TO GIVE US A TEST — SHE CAN'T, NOW!

CONGRATULATIONS, NICOLA. AND THAT'S QUITE A COINCIDENCE — I WAS ABOUT TO GIVE YOU ALL A TEST ON ANOTHER ELIZABETH — QUEEN ELIZABETH THE FIRST! YOU'RE JUST IN TIME TO JOIN IN!

DOESN'T GERTIE *EVER* GET THE CHRISTMAS SPIRIT?

"Mum, Dad, Clive and I all spent Christmas Day in the baby unit at Redvale General last year . . . it was my best Christmas ever!"

AND . . . AND THIS WILL BE LITTLE ELIZABETH'S FIRST PROPER CHRISTMAS AND, AND I MAY NOT BE THERE TO SEE IT . . .

CHEER UP, NIK!

REMEMBER WHEN OLD BULLINGHAM DRESSED UP AS SANTA TO SERVE THE FIFTH YEARS THEIR DINNER?

THAT'S A TRADITION AT REDVALE COMP. THE HEAD SERVES THE FIFTH 'COS ALL YEAR ROUND THE FIFTH SERVE THE TEACHERS.

I'LL LET YOU INTO A SECRET. HE'D FORGOTTEN HIS BEARD THAT DAY. IN THE STAFFROOM, WE HAD TO MAGIC UP A QUICK BEARD OUT OF COTTON WOOL AND I GLUED IT ON FOR HIM . . . AND IT TOOK HIM HOURS TO SOAK IT OFF AFTERWARDS!

HA! HA! HA!

116

REMEMBER OUR FIRST YEAR AT THE COMP, MR COLE? WE PUT ON A PANTO — ALADDIN IN TEN MINUTES!

I'D RATHER FORGET IT, THANKS!

OH, YOU WERE BRILLIANT AS ABANAZER THE VILLAIN, SIR!

AND WHAT ABOUT HODGE AND FREDDY AS WIDOW TWANKY AND WISHEE WASHEE?

THE BEST PART WAS YOU TWINS AS THE HORSE WHEN YOU DID THAT DANCE —

— AND YOUR COSTUME SPLIT 'COS ONE OF YOU WENT THE WRONG WAY!

HA! HA! HA!

HA! HA! HA!

THAT WAS HAYLEY, AT THE BACK!

IT WAS NOT! IT WAS BECKY, UP THE FRONT!

SSH! LISTEN! CAN YOU GUYS HEAR SOMETHING?

IT'S A HELICOPTER! IS IT COMING HERE?

I DOUBT IT CAN LAND IN THIS WEATHER, LAURA.

LOOK — IN THE COPTER! IT'S *SANTA*!

HE'S DROPPED SOMETHING BY PARACHUTE!

Mr Cole went outside for the crate—

SUPPLIES! FOOD AND LIGHT FOR THE STRANDED! GOOD OLD SANTA!

AND . . . PRESENTS!

WITH OUR NAMES ON, LOOK!

A SILVER CHARM FOR MY CHARM BRACELET!

GREAT! A REAL FOUNTAIN PEN — I ALWAYS WANTED ONE OF THESE!

MMM! MY FAVOURITE BATH SOAP!

The girls spent a happy night, and next morning—

GOOD NEWS, GIRLS! THE WEATHER'S EASED OFF AND THE RIVER'S DOWN ENOUGH FOR A LAND ROVER TO GET THROUGH.

THEN WE'RE GOING HOME, AFTER ALL!

HOORAY!

So, soon—

THIS LOOKED LIKE BEING A DISASTROUS CHRISTMAS — BUT IT'S BEEN REALLY GOOD FUN!

ESPECIALLY WHEN SANTA CAME!

I WONDER WHO THAT SANTA WAS?

OH, SOME MEMBER OF A MOUNTAIN RESCUE TEAM, I GUESS.

RIGHT. BUT I'VE BEEN THINKING . . . HOW DID HE KNOW ALL OUR NAMES . . . AND *EXACTLY* WHAT EACH OF US WANTED?

OO-ER! YOU DON'T THINK . . .?

THE END

Carrie's COMPUTER

ONE morning, Carrie Jones received a small parcel.

ANYTHING INTERESTING IN THE POST THIS MORNING, MUM?

THERE'S A PACKAGE FOR YOU, CARRIE. LOOKS LIKE IT'S FROM GRAN.

IT'S A GAME FOR MY COMPUTER.

THAT'S NICE. YOU'LL HAVE TO WRITE AND THANK HER.

IT WAS KIND. TROUBLE IS, I'M NOT VERY KEEN ON COMPUTER GAMES.

That evening —

I'D BETTER TRY THIS GAME OUT, SO I CAN TELL GRAN ABOUT IT IN MY LETTER. IT'S CALLED DELIVERY GIRL. I BET IT'S BORING!

But —

IT'S REALLY GOOD! I'M A GROCER'S DELIVERY GIRL, AND I HAVE TO DELIVER BOXES OF GROCERIES TO CUSTOMERS' HOUSES. I LOSE POINTS AND LIVES IF I DROP ANY FOOD OR IF ONE OF THE HAZARDS GETS ME.

YOU SHOULD BE IN BED BY NOW. IT'S ALMOST TEN O'CLOCK.

I ONLY SAT DOWN TO PLAY THIS GAME FOR TEN MINUTES — AND THAT WAS THREE HOURS AGO. THAT SHOWS IT'S GOOD.

120

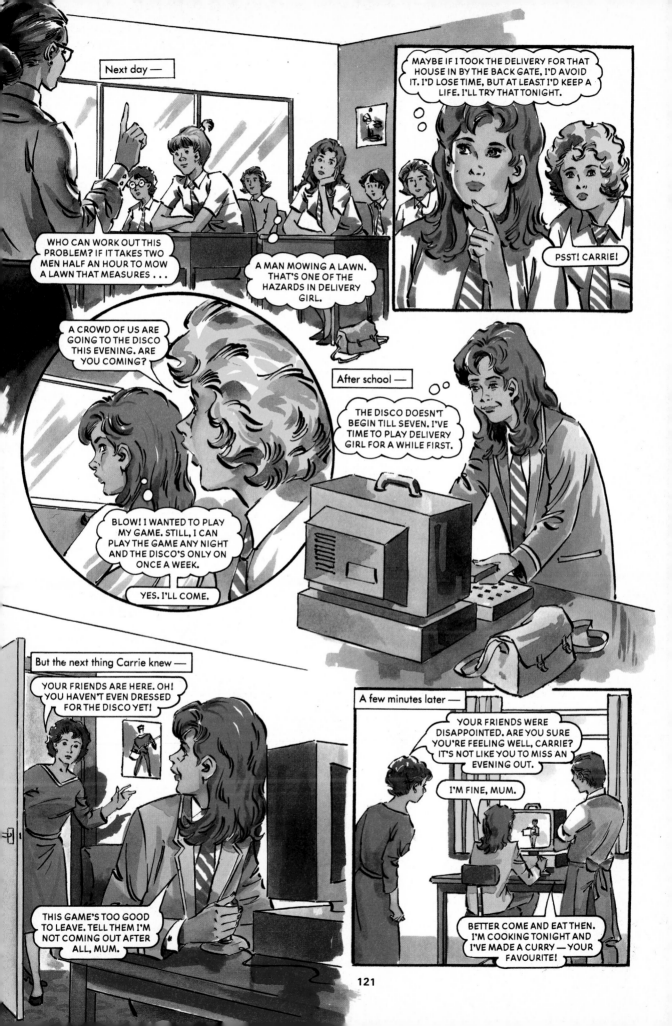

Next day —

WHO CAN WORK OUT THIS PROBLEM? IF IT TAKES TWO MEN HALF AN HOUR TO MOW A LAWN THAT MEASURES . . .

A MAN MOWING A LAWN. THAT'S ONE OF THE HAZARDS IN DELIVERY GIRL.

MAYBE IF I TOOK THE DELIVERY FOR THAT HOUSE IN BY THE BACK GATE, I'D AVOID IT. I'D LOSE TIME, BUT AT LEAST I'D KEEP A LIFE. I'LL TRY THAT TONIGHT.

PSST! CARRIE!

A CROWD OF US ARE GOING TO THE DISCO THIS EVENING. ARE YOU COMING?

After school —

THE DISCO DOESN'T BEGIN TILL SEVEN. I'VE TIME TO PLAY DELIVERY GIRL FOR A WHILE FIRST.

BLOW! I WANTED TO PLAY MY GAME. STILL, I CAN PLAY THE GAME ANY NIGHT AND THE DISCO'S ONLY ON ONCE A WEEK.

YES. I'LL COME.

But the next thing Carrie knew —

YOUR FRIENDS ARE HERE. OH! YOU HAVEN'T EVEN DRESSED FOR THE DISCO YET!

A few minutes later —

YOUR FRIENDS WERE DISAPPOINTED. ARE YOU SURE YOU'RE FEELING WELL, CARRIE? IT'S NOT LIKE YOU TO MISS AN EVENING OUT.

I'M FINE, MUM.

THIS GAME'S TOO GOOD TO LEAVE. TELL THEM I'M NOT COMING OUT AFTER ALL, MUM.

BETTER COME AND EAT THEN. I'M COOKING TONIGHT AND I'VE MADE A CURRY — YOUR FAVOURITE!

121

AH! THE DOG! HE'S HUGE! HE'S GOING TO EAT ME! HELP!

CARRIE! ARE YOU ALL RIGHT?

WHERE AM I?

PHEW! I'M ON THE FLOOR IN MY OWN ROOM. I MUST HAVE MANAGED TO JUMP OUT OF THE COMPUTER.

WHAT ARE YOU TALKING ABOUT? I THINK YOU FELL ASLEEP IN FRONT OF IT AND THEN FELL OFF THE CHAIR.

I WON'T ARGUE. WAS IT JUST A DREAM, OR DID I REALLY GET PULLED INTO THE COMPUTER FOR A WHILE? WELL, I KNOW ONE THING — WHEN YOU ACTUALLY *ARE* THE CHARACTER ON THE SCREEN, IT'S TERRIFYING!

YOU'VE BEEN OVERDOING IT. YOU'RE NOT TO SPEND SO MUCH TIME PLAYING THAT COMPUTER IN FUTURE.

OKAY, MUM.

THE END